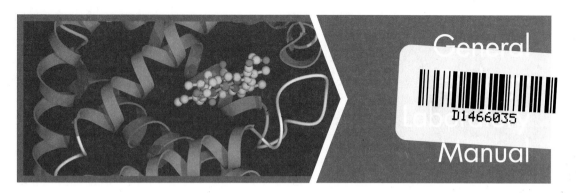

General Lab Manual

D1466035

BIOLOGY 101

SECOND EDITION
Department of Biology
Northern Virginia
Community College
Annandale Campus

CHIEF EDITOR
Ilya Tëmkin

EDITORIAL TEAM
Karen Bushaw-Newton
Paul Fitzgerald
Trudy Gillevet
Karla Henthorn
Michael Peglar
Swathi Seeke
Rebecca Wright

HAYDEN
HM
McNEIL

LabPartner materials included courtesy of
LabPartner, W. H. Freeman Publishing, and Hayden-McNeil Publishing.
www.whfreeman.com/labpartner

Victoria Nnall

Hayden-McNeil Sustainability

Hayden-McNeil's standard paper stock uses a minimum of 30% post-consumer waste. We offer higher % options by request, including a 100% recycled stock. Additionally, Hayden-McNeil Custom Digital provides authors with the opportunity to convert print products to a digital format. Hayden-McNeil is part of a larger sustainability initiative through Macmillan Higher Ed. Visit http://sustainability.macmillan.com to learn more.

Copyright © 2014 by the Department of Biology, Northern Virginia Community College, Annandale Campus

Copyright © 2014 by LabPartner, Hayden-McNeil, LLC, as noted in text

Copyright © 2014 by LabPartner, W.H. Freeman Publishing, as noted in text

Copyright © 2014 by Hayden-McNeil, LLC on illustrations provided

Photos provided by Hayden-McNeil, LLC are owned or used under license

Copyright © 2012 by Dana Kurpius and Fred Vogt, Elgin Community College for Laboratory 1, The Scientific Method and Laboratory 8, Genetics.

Copyright © 2013 by the Department of Biological Sciences, Sam Houston State University for Laboratory 2, The Microscope.

Copyright © 2012 by David Luther for Laboratory 5, Enzymes.

All rights reserved.

Permission in writing must be obtained from the publisher before any part of this work may be reproduced or transmitted in any form or by any means, electronic or mechanical, including photocopying and recording, or by any information storage or retrieval system.

Printed in the United States of America

10 9 8 7 6 5 4 3 2 1

ISBN 978-0-7380-6962-3

Hayden-McNeil Publishing
14903 Pilot Drive
Plymouth, MI 48170
www.hmpublishing.com

Temkin 6962-3 F14

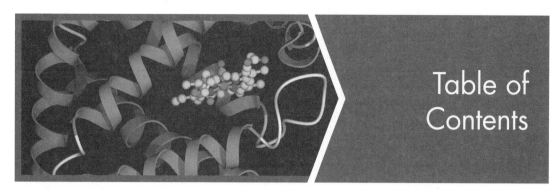

Table of Contents

BIOLOGY 101

1
The Scientific Method

OBJECTIVES

After completing this lab, you should be able to:

+ Demonstrate proficiency in relevant equipment.

+ Distinguish between qualitative and quantitative data.

+ Explain the steps of the scientific method.

+ Design a basic experiment using the established scientific protocol.

+ Construct and analyze a graph.

INTRODUCTION

Science

Science comes from the Latin word *scientia*, which means knowledge. As scientists, there are two ways to obtain knowledge about how the natural world works: discovery science and hypothesis-driven science. Throughout scientific history many individuals have relied on discovery science to further understanding of observed phenomena. This kind of science is based on making observations about the natural world, recording them, and drawing conclusions based off the gathered information. For example, Charles Darwin made many observations about various organisms (both extinct and extant) that ultimately led him to develop his conclusion that organisms evolve by natural selection.

While it is true that discovery science can change the world (think Darwin), most scientific inquiry performed in modern times is hypothesis-driven science. This process differs in that

Adapted from *Biology 108 Laboratory Manual*, copyright © 2012 by Dana Kurpius and Fred Vogt, Elgin Community College as modified by the Department of Biology, Northern Virginia Community College, Annandale Campus. Additional duplication is prohibited without written permission of Hayden-McNeil, LLC and Dana Kurpius and Fred Vogt.

a researcher takes the observation made during discovery science and asks a question about it. At this point a scientist is no longer content with making simple observations; rather, they are attempting to explain the observed phenomenon by asking questions that can be tested. The acquisition of scientific knowledge using hypothesis-driven science is a process that comprises several steps. Taken together, the systematic process of asking questions and seeking answers about the natural world is known as the scientific method.

Scientific Method

The scientific method is a process for developing and testing predictions based off of observed phenomena. When used correctly, the scientific method provides conclusions that are verifiable and repeatable. In general, the primary components of the scientific method include an observation, a question, a hypothesis, a prediction, and the experiment. It is likely that you have used components of the scientific method in your daily life without realizing it, in a procedure similar to troubleshooting. For example, your car does not start in the morning. Is it the battery? Is it the starter? Is it out of gas? You will likely ask yourself these obvious questions based off the initial observation that your car is not starting. This philosophy uses your everyday knowledge regarding the topic in an attempt to answer the questions.

Observation

Hypothesis-driven science always begins with an observation as in the example of your car not starting or the observation that bacteria do not seem to grow as fast in the refrigerator. Observations always lead to the next step in the scientific method, which is a question.

Question

The question is always derived from the observation. Using the previous example, you would ask, "why is my car not starting?" or, "why do bacteria grow slower in colder temperatures?" The question is going to drive the process such that a researcher will design an experiment to answer it. When a question is asked, what do you expect to receive? Obviously, an answer is expected. However, in science, the investigator calls the answer to a question a hypothesis.

Hypothesis

Classically, a hypothesis is defined as an educated guess. This is because people formulate answers based on personal knowledge and experience regarding the topic. Ultimately, a hypothesis is nothing more or less than an answer to a question. A hypothesis must be a stated answer that is both testable and falsifiable. Many statements may seem like a hypothesis; however, there is no way to collect and analyze data, thus ruling it out as an acceptable hypothesis. One inappropriate example could be that you state your car is a piece of junk.

Explain why the stated hypothesis is invalid.

With the previous example, a valid hypothesis could be that the car battery is dead. What would a possible hypothesis be for the observation that bacteria do not grow as well at colder temperatures?

Prediction

A prediction is a more detailed hypothesis. Specifically, a prediction includes not only the hypothesis, but also the game plan and predicted result. In general, the prediction takes the form of an "if…then" statement, which is one helpful way to identify predictions. The "if…then" statement provides a particular outcome based on the logical argument in the prediction. For example, an appropriate prediction to the previous example would be *if* the car battery is dead and I replace it, *then* my car will start. Notice the example prediction includes: the hypothesis, what will be done to test it, and the predicted result.

What would a possible prediction be for the observation that bacteria do not grow as well at colder temperatures?

Experiment

The experiment portion will be where a procedure is designed to test the validity of the hypothesis. In science, this systematic process is referred to as a controlled experiment. Any such experiment should have the following components: an experimental group and control group.

The role of the control group is to remain unchanged; therefore serving as a basis of comparison for the experimental group. In contrast, the experimental group is going to be manipulated to assess your hypothesis. In other words, the experimental group will receive the treatment, which allows a comparison of the results to the control group.

Pretend you are in charge of a study for a drug that is thought to lower blood pressure. Next, you have defined the two groups and populated them with individuals appropriate to the study. In addition to the difference of the drug treatment, would it be a good idea if the two groups also slept for different amounts of time, ate totally different foods, got different amounts of exercise, and had differences in alcohol and smoking habits? It is likely someone would say no to all of the above questions.

Why?

A variable is any factor or condition that can vary. Specifically, in a controlled experiment a variable would be any factor that could vary between the two groups. In addition to the two groups, any good scientific study should have three general kinds of variables that are manipulated or controlled: independent variable, dependent variable, and the control or standard variables.

The independent variable is the *one* factor that the scientist changes between the two groups. Specifically, the independent variable is being tested for causation. In fact, it can be thought of as the hypothesis. From the previous example of the drug study, the independent variable is the blood pressure medication.

What would be the independent variable from the example of the bacteria?

If you were the lead scientist in the drug study, how would the effectiveness of the drug be determined? In other words, how can a researcher assess whether or not their stated hypothesis was correct? At this point, the dependent variable would be analyzed. This particular variable is going to change in response to the independent variable and determine the conclusion. In the drug study, differences in blood pressure between the two groups are dependent upon the medication.

How can one have confidence that any difference in blood pressures between the two groups is due to the drug?

What would be the dependent variable from the example of the bacteria?

All other factors that need to be kept identical between the two groups are collectively termed the control/standard variables. From the example of the bacteria, control variables would include strain of bacteria, growth media, culture plate material, moisture, and temperature.

Identify three control/standard variables from the blood pressure medication study.

Experiments can generate two types of data: quantitative and qualitative results. Quantitative data are results with assigned values, such as temperature. In contrast, qualitative data are descriptive results, such as color.

Using the following table, provide examples of each kind of data using the bacteria experiment as your guide.

Table 1-1. *Types of scientific data.*

Qualitative Data	Quantitative Data

Graphing

Data are typically placed into an easy-to-interpret visual form called a graph. There are rules for the placement of variables on specific axes of a graph. For instance, the dependent variable is always graphed on the Y-axis, while the independent variable is placed on the X-axis. When making a graph, there must be a description of the dependent variable along the Y-axis that includes a unit of measure and an expressive title.

Drug X Increases Cell Branch Length

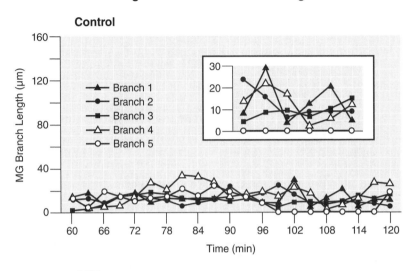

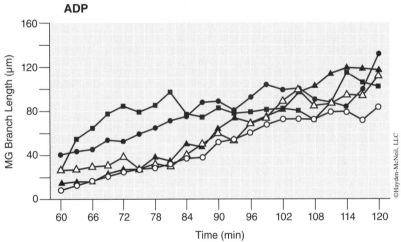

Activity 1

Materials

- Balance
- Mortar and pestle
- 10 mL graduated cylinder
- 20 mL beaker
- Distilled H_2O (dH_2O)
- Apple
- Lemon
- Potato
- Knife (scalpel or razor blade)
- Cutting board
- pH paper
- Blood pressure cuff (optional)

PROCEDURE

You will demonstrate an understanding of the scientific method by measuring the pH of the apple, lemon, and potato. In short, pH measures the acidity of a solution. The pH scale has a range of values between 0 and 14, where 0 is the most acidic, 14 is the most basic, and 7 is neutral. The lab instructor will demonstrate proper use of the equipment necessary for completion of the lab.

1. Using the graduated cylinder, measure 15 mL of dH_2O.

   Using Figure 1-1, what is the volume of fluid in the graduated cylinder?

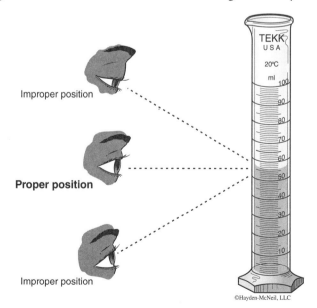

Figure 1-1.

2. Pour the contents of the graduated cylinder into a beaker and measure the pH of dH_2O.

   dH_2O pH:

   (Record your results in Table 1-2.)

3. Using the electronic balance, knife, and cutting board at your workstation, measure 15 grams of apple.

4. Dice the apple into segments that measure approximately 5 mm in width.

5. Place the diced apple into the mortar and add 15 mL of dH_2O from step 2.

6. Grind the apple into a slurry using the pestle.

7. Pour the slurry into a container (a Petri dish or a beaker).

8. Measure the slurry's pH with the provided indicator paper.

   Apple pH:

9. Record your results in Table 1-2.

10. Thoroughly rinse the knife, cutting board, mortar and pestle, beaker, and graduated cylinder.

11. Repeat steps 3–8 for lemon and potato, and record your data in Table 1-2.

THE SCIENTIFIC METHOD:
Activity 1

Name

Date

Section

1. What is the first step in the scientific method?

2. How do these items differ in their flavor?

    Apple:

    Lemon:

    Potato:

3. Taking pH into account, write a hypothesis that could account for the difference in taste.

    Hypothesis:

4. Why did you take the pH of the dH_2O?

5. What are the independent and dependent variables in this experiment?

6. List three standardized variables in this experiment.

7. What is the importance of these standards?

8. In step 10 of the procedure, what was the purpose of thoroughly cleaning the equipment?

Table 1-2. *Types of scientific data.*

Water pH	Apple pH	Lemon pH	Potato pH

9. What can you conclude from the data?

10. Will you accept or reject your hypothesis? Explain.

Activity 2

In this experiment, your pulse rate will be measured at rest and while under light exercise. Using the data you have collected, construct a graph depicting how heart rate changes in response to physical activity.

PROCEDURE

Develop a hypothesis to answer what happens to heart rate during physical activity.

1. Measure your pulse (manually or using the pressure cuff) while at rest and record this value in Table 1-3.

2. Wait one minute and measure your pulse a second time. Record this value in Table 1-3.

3. Perform step 2 two more times to complete Table 1-3.

4. Calculate your average resting pulse and record it in Table 1-3.

5. Go to the nearest stairwell and briskly climb the stairs.

6. Measure your pulse and record it in Table 1-3.

7. Wait one minute and climb the stairs a second time, measure your pulse, and record it in Table 1-3.

8. Perform step 7 two more times to complete Table 1-3.

9. Calculate your average pulse rate from exercising and record it in Table 1-3.

10. Add your data to the chart that your instructor has constructed on the front board.

11. Calculate averages and percent change in heart rate.

$$\% \text{ change} = \frac{(\text{new value} - \text{old value})}{\text{old value}} \times 100\%$$

12. Complete Tables 1-4 and 1-5 using the data on the front board.

13. Construct the following graphs using the pool of class data and supplied graph paper. Be sure you clearly label each axis and provide a title for each graph.

    a. Your personal change in heart rate.

    b. Overall change in class heart rate and change in heart rate versus males and females.

THE SCIENTIFIC METHOD:
Activity 2

Name

Date

Section

Table 1-3. *Individual pulse rate while resting and exercising.*

Trial	Pulse at Rest	Pulse After Exercise
1		
2		
3		
4		
Average		

Table 1-4. *Collective female pulse rate while resting and exercising.*

Student	Average Pulse at Rest	Average Pulse After Exercise
1		
2		
3		
4		
5		
6		
7		
8		
9		
10		
11		
12		
13		
14		
15		
16		
17		
18		
19		
20		
Average		
% Change		

Table 1-5. *Collective male pulse rate while resting and exercising.*

Student	Average Pulse at Rest	Average Pulse After Exercise
1		
2		
3		
4		
5		
6		
7		
8		
9		
10		
11		
12		
13		
14		
15		
16		
17		
18		
19		
20		
Average		
% Change		

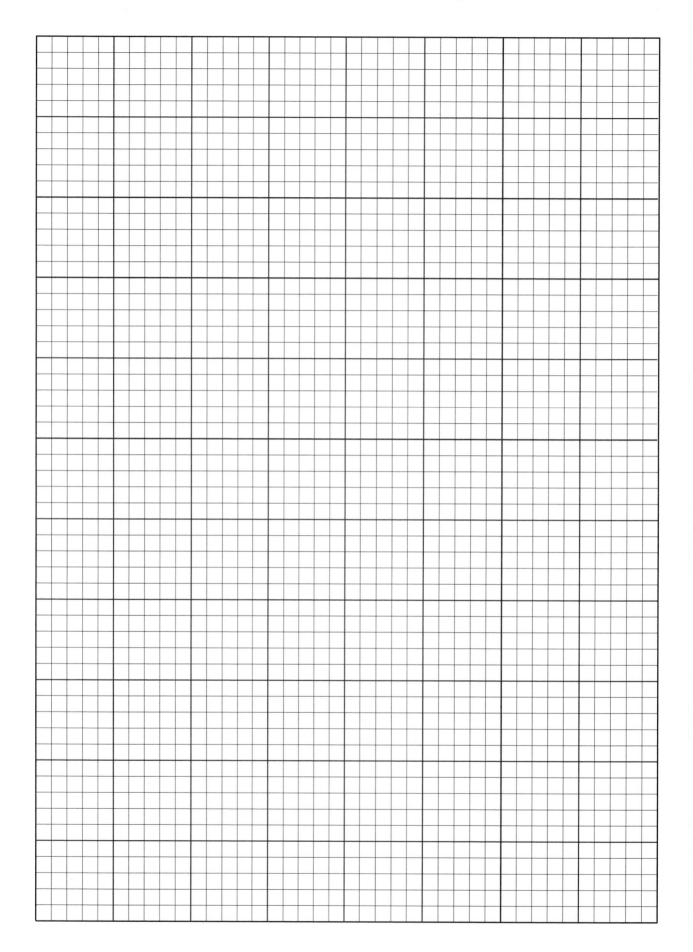

1. What are the dependent and independent variables in this experiment?

2. What are three sources of error in this experiment?

3. How would you redesign this experiment to better control for the sources of error?

4. Answer the following questions using the graphs:

   a. What was the percent change in your heart rate?

   b. What was the percent change in heart rate for the class?

   c. What was the percent change in heart rate for male vs. female?

5. Do you think the data collected would vary depending on the time of day the experiment was performed? Explain.

6. You are a newly employed "hotshot" lab technician at a fertilizer company. Your boss tasks you with evaluating the effectiveness of a new formulation of an older fertilizer. The company supplies you with two cornfields of 2,000 acres and plenty of fertilizer. Design an experiment using all aspects of the scientific method. Be sure to clearly define your groups and other components (such as: the dependent variable, independent variable, and standards/controls) of the scientific method. Assume there is an outcome to this experiment after six months of experimentation. You may decide if the experiment produces positive or negative results. However, *define* and *describe* all aspects for full credit. It may be helpful to draw a graph or two.

    a. What hypothesis is being tested?

    b. What is the independent variable and dependent variable?

    c. Describe what the control group is.

    d. List six elements of this experiment that must be controlled between the experimental and control groups.

    e. Draw a graph that shows that this new formula of fertilizer is successful at growing more corn.

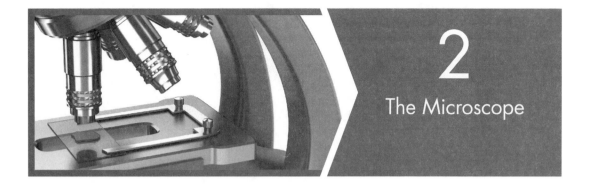

2

The Microscope

OBJECTIVES

After completing this lab, you should be able to:

+ Competently identify microscope components and their functions.

+ Use and care for the compound light microscope.

+ Prepare a wet mount of a specimen.

INTRODUCTION

Your awareness of the world around you depends upon your ability to sense it. For example, in order for you to detect a particular sound, that sound must be of a wavelength, frequency, and amplitude to stimulate your auditory nerve thereby sending a message to your brain. Likewise, you would not be able to see an object if it were too small or the wavelengths of light reflecting from it did not fall within a range detectable by your eyes. Since a great deal of scientific investigation requires observation of phenomena outside the realm of human sensibility, technological advances have extended the range of humans' sensory organs. One such advance is the microscope.

The microscope you will be using in this lab is a **compound, bright field light microscope**. Compound meaning that there is more than one lens between your eye and the object you are viewing; bright field because the object is between your eye and the light source. Light is transmitted through and around the object so that it appears darker than the bright field of light around it.

Adapted from *Biology 114 Laboratory Manual for Contemporary Biology*, 2008–2009 ed., by the Department of Biological Science, Sam Houston State University as modified by Ilya Tëmkin. Copyright © 2009 by Hayden-McNeil, LLC. Additional duplication is prohibited without written permission of Hayden-McNeil, LLC.

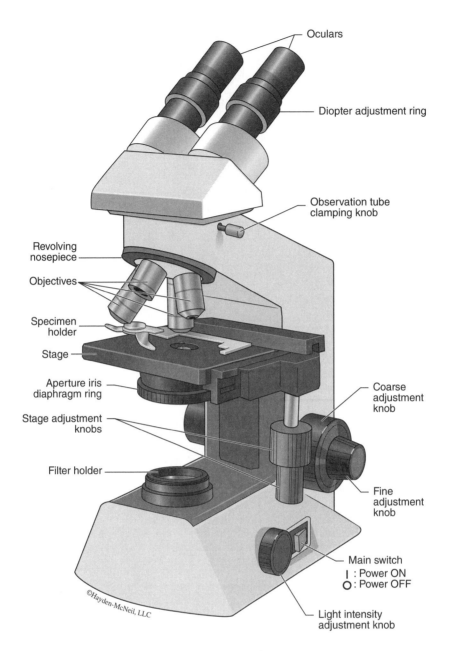

Oculars

Diopter adjustment ring

Observation tube
clamping knob

Revolving
nosepiece

Objectives

Specimen
holder

Stage

Aperture iris
diaphragm ring

Stage adjustment
knobs

Filter holder

Coarse
adjustment
knob

Fine
adjustment
knob

Main switch
I : Power ON
O : Power OFF

Light intensity
adjustment knob

©Hayden-McNeil, LLC

Figure 2-1. *Compound light microscope.*

Table 2-1. *Functions of the components of the compound microscope.*

Component	Function
Stage	Holds the slide.
Stage adjustment knobs	Move the slide forward, backward, and side to side.
Sub stage lamp	Is the source of illumination.
Sub stage condenser	Concentrates the light from the light source into a cone of light.
Iris diaphragm	Controls the amount of light entering through the aperture of the stage.
Objectives	Form a magnified image.
Revolving nose piece	Holds the objectives. Can be rotated to select and position a particular objective to the center of the stage.
Oculars (eye pieces)	Used to view the image of the specimen and to magnify the image.
Coarse adjustment knob	Helps in focusing the image by moving the stage upward or downward. To be used only when working with 4× and 10× objectives.
Fine adjustment knobs	Used to sharpen the focus of the image. Makes very fine adjustments to the position of the stage.

Activity 1: Care of Compound Microscope

Materials

+ Compound microscope
+ Lens paper
+ Lens cleaning solution
+ Letter "e" slide
+ Colored threads slide

The compound light microscope is an expensive and delicate instrument requiring gentle handling.

+ Never drag the microscope across the table top or attempt to carry it to another location in the lab room using only one hand.

+ Always carry the microscope using both hands. Use one hand to grasp the arm of the microscope and support the base of the microscope with your other hand.

+ Use only lens paper and lens cleaning solution to clean the lenses.

+ When you are finished using the scope, always: turn it off, unplug it and fold the cord, remove all slides and debris, clean the lenses with lens paper and lens cleaning solution, and rotate the nosepiece so the empty lens space or the shortest objective lens is directly over the stage aperture.

The Compound Light Microscope Components and Their Functions

Refer to Figure 2-1 when attempting to locate microscope components during this exercise.

Locate the following parts on the compound microscope:

+ Base, arm, stage

+ Sub stage lamp, sub stage condenser, iris diaphragm

+ Nose piece, 4×, 10×, 40×, and 100× objectives

+ Oculars (eye piece)

+ Stage adjustment knobs, light intensity adjustment knob, coarse adjustment knob, fine adjustment knob

Use of Compound Microscope

1. Obtain the microscopic slide labeled "Letter e". Observe the slide with your unaided eye. (Do not place it on the microscope, yet!) In the space provided on page 27, draw the letter "e" showing its actual size and orientation as it appears on the slide.

2. Plug in the microscope assigned to you.

3. Press the main switch to "|" (ON) and adjust the brightness with the light intensity adjustment knob.

4. Place the microscope slide labeled "Letter e" in the specimen holder on the stage. Make sure the specimen holder holds the slide in place securely. The label on the slide should be on your left-hand side and in the proper reading orientation. Notice the feed knobs (stage adjustment knobs) below the right-hand side of the stage. These knobs will move the specimen backwards and forwards as well as side to side. Use these stage adjustment knobs to center the letter "e" over the aperture of the stage.

5. Rotate the revolving nosepiece, lining up the shortest objective lens vertically in the light path.

6. While looking through the ocular lenses, bring the specimen into focus using the coarse adjustment knob. You will be turning the coarse adjustment knob slowly, until the letter "e" is visible and is in sharp focus. If the letter is not visible, make sure the "e" is centered over the aperture and repeat the process again.

7. Further adjust the light with the aperture iris diaphragm ring.

8. In the space provided on page 27, draw the letter "e" as seen under the scanning (4×) objective.

9. Now rotate the 10× objective into the vertical position in the light path and once again focus with the coarse adjustment knob. You may also need to adjust the light intensity.

10. Draw the letter "e" as seen under the low power (10×) objective.

11. To use the high power objective (40×), you would rotate the nosepiece until the 40× lens is in the vertical position in the light path. Notice the distance between the slide and the 40× objective is very little. Use ONLY the FINE FOCUS ADJUSTMENT KNOB with the 40× objective. Always adjust the light for optimal viewing.

12. Draw the letter "e" as seen under the high power (40×) objective.

13. Rotate the nosepiece to bring the scanning objective (4×) to the center.

14. Replace the "e" slide with the slide labeled "colored threads."

15. Looking through the oculars lens, bring the colored threads on the slide to focus under the 4× objective. You should be able to see all three colored threads at the same time.

16. Looking through the oculars, use the stage adjustment knob to move the slide so that the intersection of the three colored threads is at the center of your field of vision. Now, switch to the 10× objective and bring the specimen to focus. If all three colored threads are not in sharp focus, use the fine adjustment knob. Observe the order in which the colored threads go in and out of focus. Switch to the 40× objective. Use the fine adjustment to get at least one colored thread into sharp focus. Answer questions 9 and 10 on page 29.

Preparation of Wet Mounts

When observing a fresh specimen or a living culture, the wet mount technique is performed to prevent the specimen from drying out.

Materials

- Clean microscopic slides
- Plastic dropper
- Distilled water
- A leaf from the water plant, *Elodea*
- Coverslips
- Toothpicks
- Methylene blue dye

PROCEDURE

1. Use a plastic dropper to transfer a drop of water onto a clean microscope slide.

2. Place a leaf of *Elodea* on the drop of water.

3. Carefully place a coverslip on the drop of water. Try not to trap air bubbles under the coverslip. Refer to Figure 2-2 for a visual.

4. Place the slide in the specimen holder of the microscope stage. Observe the wet mount first with the 4× objective lens, then with the 10× and 40× lenses.

5. Sketch your observations at each magnification on page 29.

6. Now, prepare a wet mount of human cheek cells by gently scraping the inside of your cheek with a toothpick and mixing the scrapings on the toothpick in a drop of water or drop of methylene blue dye on a clean slide. Remember to place a coverslip on the preparation. Sketch your observation as seen under the 40× objective.

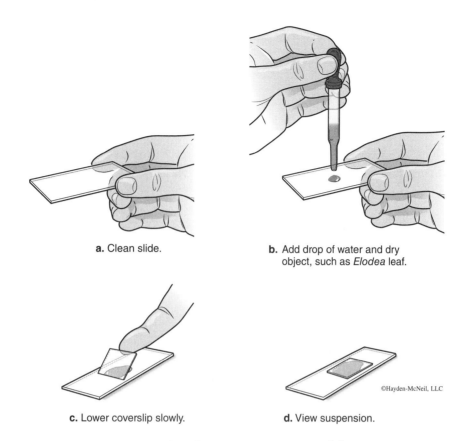

a. Clean slide.

b. Add drop of water and dry object, such as *Elodea* leaf.

c. Lower coverslip slowly.

d. View suspension.

©Hayden-McNeil, LLC

Figure 2-2. *Preparing a wet mount slide.*

THE MICROSCOPE

INQUIRY AND ANALYSIS

Name

Date

Section

1. Letter "e" as seen with unaided eye:

2. Letter "e" as seen under the following three objective lenses:

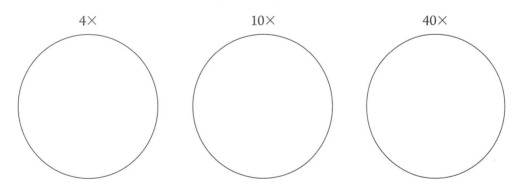

4×   10×   40×

3. Were you able to see the letter "e" completely under the 40× objective? What does it tell you about the relationship between field of vision and magnification?

4. Why should a specimen seen through the oculars be centered in the field of vision before switching to focus from low power objective to high power objective?

The distance between the slide and the objective, when the specimen is in focus, is known as the working distance.

5. Which objective lens has the greatest working distance?

6. Which objective lens has the least working distance?

7. What appears to be the relationship between working distance and magnification?

The ocular lenses and the objective lens magnify the image seen under the microscope. The magnifying power of the objective is multiplied by the magnifying power of the ocular ($10\times$) to calculate the total magnification.

8. What is the total magnification achieved when viewing the letter "e" through the following objectives?

   a. Scanning objective

   b. Low power objective

   c. High power objective

9. When you were observing the slide labeled "colored threads", were you able to clearly focus all three colored threads at the same time? Which objective enabled you to see all three colors in focus at the same time?

10. Can you determine which colored thread is on top? Which colored thread is at the bottom? How did you determine this?

11. *Elodea* leaf as seen under the following objectives:

4× 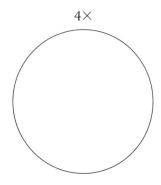   10× 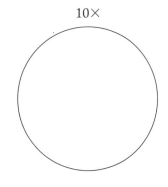   40×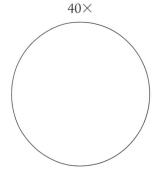

12. Human cheek cell as seen under the following objectives:

10× 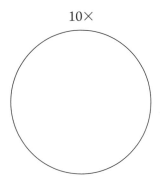   40×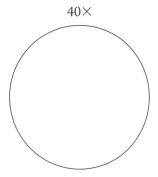

3

Diversity

OBJECTIVES

After completing this lab, you should be able to:

+ Recognize the different morphological forms of bacteria.

+ Identify and classify representative protozoans, fungi (slime molds), and algae.

INTRODUCTION

Biologists currently recognize three domains of living things: **Bacteria**, **Archaea**, and **Eukarya**. The domain Bacteria is comprised of one kingdom, **Eubacteria** (true bacteria). The domain Archaea is also composed of one kingdom, **Archaebacteria** (ancient bacteria). The domain Eukarya includes all other living organisms: kingdoms **Protista** (unicellular animals and plants, slime molds, and algae), **Fungi**, **Plantae** (multicellular plants), and **Animalia** (multicellular animals).

Among the diverse organisms in these kingdoms you will find two major types. **Prokaryotes** are unicellular (single-celled) organisms characterized by the absence of a membrane-bound nucleus and membrane-bound organelles. In contrast, **eukaryotes** have both a well-formed nucleus and many other types of membrane-bound organelles.

Prokaryotes and eukaryotes differ also in the chemical composition of their cell walls (if present), the organization of their genetic material, and the structure of their flagella. The kingdoms **Eubacteria** and **Archaebacteria** are composed of prokaryotic organisms. Eukaryotic organisms are found in the other four kingdoms.

Adapted from *Biology in the Laboratory*, 3rd ed., by Doris R. Helms, Carl W. Helms, Robert J. Kosinski, and John R. Cummings as modified by Ilya Tëmkin. Copyright © 1998 by W.H. Freeman and Company. Additional duplication is prohibited without written permission of W.H. Freeman and Company.

PART I: DOMAINS BACTERIA AND ARCHAEA

Prokaryotes represent the oldest and simplest living things. Prokaryotes are clearly different from eukaryotes, but ordering them taxonomically into subgroups of organisms according to anatomical and physiological affinities is difficult. Based on comparison of DNA and RNA sequences, it appears that prokaryotes diverged early in evolutionary history into two distinct lineages now recognized as domains, Bacteria and Archaea (Figure 3-1).

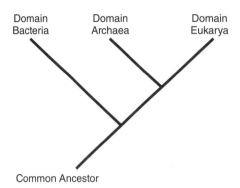

Figure 3-1. *According to present thinking, the domains Eukarya and Archaea share a common ancestry and thus are more closely related to each other than to the domain Bacteria.*

Bacteria are virtually ubiquitous. Not only do bacteria surround you, they thrive within you. Most of these bacteria are nonpathogenic and actually keep your body free from more harmful bacteria through competition. However, conditions sometimes make the difference between a pathogen and a nonpathogen. For example, *Staphylococcus aureus*, a common bacterium, can cause severe infections if introduced into an open cut. The same bacterium is also thought to be an agent in toxic shock syndrome.

Other bacteria play a large role in the environment and in the economy. Some bacteria are important as decomposers, recycling dead material into components required by living organisms. In sewage treatment plants, they promote the breakdown of solid wastes. Many foods, such as vinegar, sour cream, yogurt, and cheeses, are made with the help of bacteria. Certain antibiotics are produced by bacteria. Some bacteria can even be used to clean up oil spills. Bacteria are also a main focus of genetic and biochemical research.

MATERIALS

+ Microscope
+ Microscopic slides
+ Living specimens
+ Lens cleaning solution

Activity 1: Bacteria

Most bacteria may be classified into one of three major morphological groups: rods (bacilli), spheres (cocci), or spirals (spirilla). You can observe the morphology of these groups both microscopically and macroscopically, by observing growth forms.

PROCEDURE

1. Check the demonstration microscopes and observe the basic morphological forms of bacteria (Figure 3-2). Draw the bacterial forms and identify each in the space that follows.

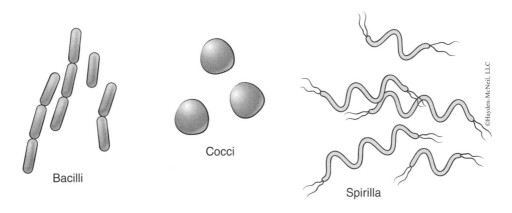

Bacilli   Cocci   Spirilla

Figure 3-2. *Morphology of bacteria.*

Demonstration A   **Demonstration B**   **Demonstration C**

Type _____   Type _____   Type _____

a. Strep throat is caused by streptococcal bacteria. What shape would you expect these bacteria to have?

b. The prefix "strep" means strip or chain. How would you expect streptococcal bacteria to be arranged?

c. How are the bacterial cells arranged in the demonstration slides you have observed? As single cells? Clusters? Strands? A _____ B _____ C _____

Activity 2: Cyanobacteria

Traditionally, cyanobacteria have been called "blue-green algae." However, they are not algae, but prokaryotes: Gram-negative photosynthetic bacteria. Cyanobacteria contain chlorophyll *a* (as do photosynthetic eukaryotic green plants and algae), but it is characteristically masked by blue, red, and purple pigments. These pigments (**phycobilins**) enhance light absorption by the cells and serve as nitrogen reservoirs. All cyanobacteria are unicellular, but individual cells are commonly attached to each other by a gelatinous sheath, thus producing filaments or colonies. Like some other bacteria, many cyanobacteria are able to fix atmospheric nitrogen.

Cyanobacteria share with other bacteria the ability to inhabit the most inhospitable locations on earth, such as hot springs and bare rocks. Cyanobacteria can be desiccated for many years yet resume growth when water is again present.

PROCEDURE

Prepare and examine material on a wet-mount slide and then exchange slides with your partner. Depending on the material available, examine one or more examples of cyanobacteria. Refer to Table 3-1, and add further information to the table where necessary. Make sketches if instructed to do so, adding labels where possible.

Most cells of cyanobacteria are structurally undistinguished, but a few specialized cell types can be recognized. **Heterocysts** are round or oval, *clear* cells that allow cyanobacteria to fix atmospheric nitrogen. Many cyanobacteria can fix nitrogen when they are in an anaerobic environment, but heterocysts are necessary for aerobic nitrogen fixation. **Akinetes** are generally larger, usually oval, densely packed, sporelike reproductive cells that are resistant to adverse conditions.

Table 3-1. *Characteristics of cyanobacteria.*

Type	Morphology	Distinctive features
Nostoc 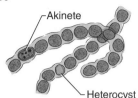	Filaments of round cells; gelatinous sheath surrounds filament.	Can combine in large gelatinous balls containing hundreds of filaments. Reproduce by fission or fragmentation.
Cylindrospermum 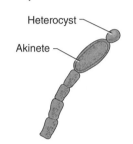	Filaments of rectangular cells; length greater than width.	**Heterocysts** at the ends of filaments function in nitrogen fixation. Reproduce by fission or fragmentaton. **Akinetes** are special sporelike reproductive cells resistant to adverse environmental conditions.
Oscillatoria 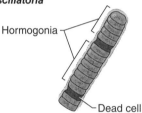	Filaments of rectangular cells covered by a sheath; width greater than length.	Oscillate, seek specific conditions in water. Reproduce by fragmentation only. **Hormogonia** are short fragments between dead cells where fragmentation takes place.
Anabaena 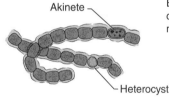	Barrel-shaped vegetative cells held in a gelatinous matrix.	Heterocysts are integral or terminal and function in nitrogen fixation. Reproduce by fission or fragmentation. Akinetes are dispersed among vegetative cells.
Gleocapsa 	Spherical cells; single or groups of 2 to 8; each cell surrounded by its own sheath; colony surrounded by sheath.	Can fix nitrogen despite absence of heterocysts. Reproduce by fission.

©Hayden-McNeil, LLC

Sketches

a. What are the basic cyanobacterial cell shapes? How are these individual cells combined to form colonies and filaments?

b. Which of the specialized cell types can you recognize in each of the types of cyanobacteria? What does the presence of these cells (heterocysts, akinetes) indicate about the environment of these organisms?

c. Cyanobacteria grow prolifically in streams and lakes with low oxygen levels and high nutrient concentrations. How might the presence or absence of cyanobacteria be used as an index of pollution in lakes?

d. How can you determine, from your microscope observations, whether cyanobacteria are prokaryotes or eukaryotes?

Name three differences between prokaryotes and eukaryotes.

PART II: KINGDOM PROTISTA

With the kingdom Protista,* we begin our study of eukaryotes. The cells of eukaryotic organisms contain both a nucleus and membrane-bound organelles. All other eukaryotic organisms (including fungi, plants, and animals) probably originated from the primitive protists.

For our purposes, protists can be divided into three broad groups, usually based on modes of nutrition.

Protozoa Unicellular heterotrophs, typically animal-like.

Fungus-like protists (slime molds) Sometimes referred to as the "lower fungi" because they may be multinucleate, as are fungi, during some part of their life cycle. They are classified with protists because of their similarities to protozoans.

Algae Unicellular and multicellular plant-like organisms.

PROTOZOA

Protozoans are unicellular organisms. Most are motile. Protozoans can be found in free-living and parasitic forms and in freshwater or marine environments.

---

*Originally, only unicellular organisms were assigned to the kingdom Protista, but in recent years it has been suggested that the kingdom be expanded to include some multicellular organisms—the multicellular algae and fungus-like organisms that lack some of the important characteristics of true fungi. The name Protoctista has been proposed for this "expanded kingdom."

Activity 3: Protozoa

There are many phyla of protozoans. Some of the most common forms are represented below. They can be distinguished by body form and mode of locomotion (Table 3-2).

PROCEDURE

Observe material using prepared slides or, if fresh material is available, make temporary wet-mount slides according to directions in Table 3-2. Label structures and make notes or sketches of any identifying characteristics or behaviors.

Table 3-2. *Characteristics of protozoans.*

Phylum/Representative	Method of Observation	Mode of Locomotion
Zoomastigophora *Trypanosoma* Flagellum — Undulating membrane — Nucleus — ©Hayden-McNeil, LLC	Study a prepared slide.	Flagellar movement. A single **flagellum** is united basally with the body of cell by an undulating membrane. Amoeboid extensions (**pseudopodia**) are also found in many flagellates. *Trypanosoma gambiense* is the causative agent of African sleeping sickness.
Rhizopoda *Amoeba* — Advancing pseudopods — Forming food vacuole — Food vacuole — Anal pore — Nucleus — Contractile vacuole — Withdrawing pseudopods — ©Hayden-McNeil, LLC	Examine living amoebas. You can see the organism on the bottom or side of the culture dish. Remove an amoeba with a pipette and place it on a glass slide. Observe without a coverslip. Adjust light. If motion does not occur, add coverslip.	Amoeboid movement— pseudopodia. Cytoplasmic extensions change in size.

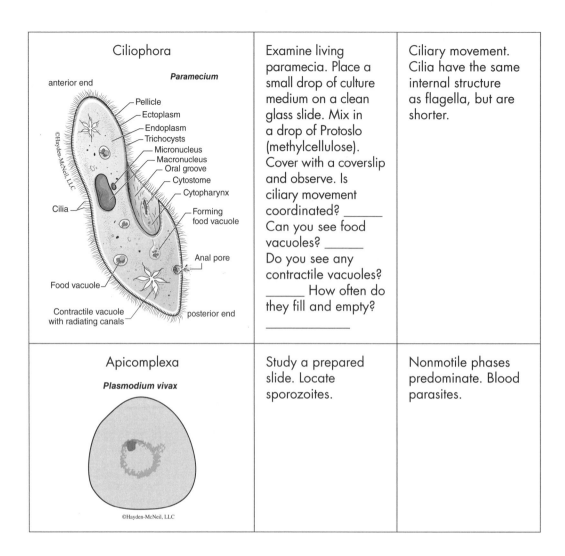

| Ciliophora | Examine living paramecia. Place a small drop of culture medium on a clean glass slide. Mix in a drop of Protoslo (methylcellulose). Cover with a coverslip and observe. Is ciliary movement coordinated? _____ Can you see food vacuoles? _____ Do you see any contractile vacuoles? _____ How often do they fill and empty? _____ | Ciliary movement. Cilia have the same internal structure as flagella, but are shorter. |
| Apicomplexa | Study a prepared slide. Locate sporozoites. | Nonmotile phases predominate. Blood parasites. |

Activity 4: Algae

You will study six phyla of algae. Representatives range in size from microscopic to extremely large. Both freshwater and marine species exist.

PROCEDURE

Obtain fresh material or prepared slides to study representatives of the six divisions of algae. Refer to Table 3-3 for characteristics and methods of observation.

Table 3-3. *Characteristics of algae.*

Phylum/Representative	Characteristics/Method of Observation
Euglenophyta *Euglena gracilis* (Diagram labeled: Flagellum, Eyespot, Reservoir, Contractile vacuole, Pellicle, Nucleus, Mitochondrion, Chloroplast) ©Hayden-McNeil, LLC	Unicellular. True eye-socket algae. **Flagellum** attached within reservoir, distinct orange-red eyespot adjacent to the flagellum. A flexible protein layer (pellicle) rather than a rigid cell wall allows the organism to change its shape. Many bright green chloroplasts. Locomotion: swimming, creeping, or floating. *Method of Observation* Make a wet mount of *Euglena*. Mix a drop of Protoslo with culture.
Chrysophyta (Diagram labeled: Diatoms) ©Hayden-McNeil, LLC	Diatoms only: Unicellular or chains of rod (**pennate**) or circular (**centric**) shapes. Cell walls of silica with numerous holes. Walls make two overlapping halves (**thecas**) that fit together like the halves of a Petri dish. Cells are brownish-yellow. Locomotion: attached, gliding, or floating. *Method of Observation* Make a wet mount of diatomaceous earth, if available, or use material collected from stream rocks.
Pyrrophyta (Dinophyta) (Diagram labeled: Transverse flagellum, Trailing flagellum, Jointed polysaccharide plates, *Peridinium*) ©Hayden-McNeil, LLC	Unicellular. Spinning flagellates. All members are biflagellate and motile. One flagellum wraps around the middle of the cell and allows it to spin; another flagellum trails and pushes the cell along. Cell wall composed of many interlocking plates, giving an armored appearance. Brownish color. Locomotion: floating or swimming. *Method of Observation* Study prepared slide of *Peridinium*.

Activity 5: Chlorophyta

It is thought that the ancestor of land plants was a green alga. Several evolutionary trends are obvious among the **Chlorophyta**, including:

+ Increase in size accompanied by **cell differentiation**. Within a group of cells, certain cells have specific functions; individual cells do not act independently.

+ Sexual reproduction. Among the algae are three types of sexual reproduction (listed from the most primitive to the most advanced):

Isogamy: Male and female gametes look exactly alike (isogametes); both are motile.

Anisogamy: Also called heterogamy. Male and female gametes look alike except that the female gamete (egg) is larger; both are motile.

Oogamy: The male gamete (sperm) is small and motile. The female gamete (egg) is large and nonmotile.

PROCEDURE

Use prepared slides or, if fresh material is available, make temporary mounts of the following organisms. Observe the progression in size and complexity illustrated in the green algae. Sketch the organisms in the spaces provided.

Chlamydomonas (class Chlorophyceae) Unicellular thallus.	*Gonium* (class Chlorophyceae) Spherical colony made up of 4 to 32 cells, depending on the species.
Volvox (class Chlorophyceae) Spherical colony made up of 500 to 50,000 cells, depending on the species.	*Zygnema* (class Chlorophyceae) Simple, unbranched filament (cell division occurs in a single plane).

Activity 6: Recognizing Protists Among the Plankton

Plankton is a general term for small (mostly microscopic) aquatic organisms found in the upper levels of water where light is abundant. Plankton includes both plant-like photosynthetic forms (*phytoplankton*) and animal-like heterotrophic forms (*zooplankton*). A sample from enriched natural water, such as a fish pond, is an excellent source of algae and protozoans, as well as microscopic animals.

PROCEDURE

1. Place a small drop of the plankton sample on a slide and add a coverslip. Your instructor will provide some illustrations of types of organisms you are likely to see.

2. Identify as many organisms as possible. Various types of algae (diatoms, desmids, and, possibly filamentous green algae) may be visible. Some of the flagellates you find may belong to the algal division Euglenophyta rather than Zoomastigophora, but they, too, illustrate the way in which flagellates in general move. Study this movement carefully.

3. Sketch representatives in the space provided below.

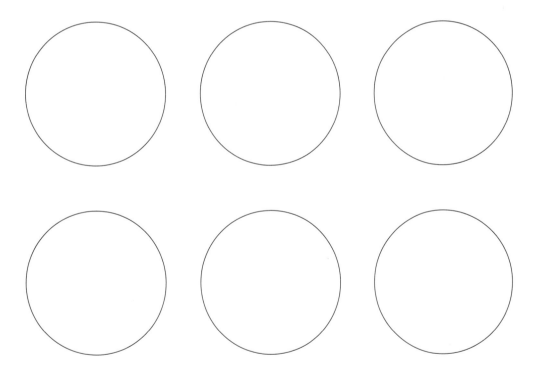

a. What might be the role of the plankton in the food chain of an ocean or lake?

b. Both phytoplankton and zooplankton can migrate to various depths in a lake or ocean. What might cause these organisms to surface or to move to greater depths within a lake or ocean environment?

4

Osmosis
and Diffusion

Adapted from Investigative Biology, *Jon Glase and Paul Ecklund, Cornell University*

OBJECTIVES

After completing this lab, you should be able to:

+   Understand the basic principles of diffusion and osmosis.

+   Observe and understand the osmotic properties of plant and animal cells.

+   Understand the permeable aspects/characteristics of cell membranes.

INTRODUCTION

In this lab, you will observe osmotic properties of plant and animal cells, and the permeation of substances through cell membranes. Recall that cell membranes are composed of a lipid bilayer, the interior of which is very hydrophobic (nonpolar). It is this hydrophobic membrane interior that limits the movement of hydrophilic (polar) substances such as water, ions, and most cellular metabolites through membranes. In 1899, Charles E. Overton demonstrated that the greater the lipid solubility of a compound, the greater is its rate of penetration through a membrane. This correlation, sometimes referred to as Overton's rule, provided one of the earliest indications that lipids are a major component of membranes. In this exercise you will observe the responses of *Elodea* leaf cells and sheep erythrocytes (red blood cells) to different osmotic environments. You will also test several alcohols with different characteristics for their ability to penetrate erythrocyte membranes.

Living cells are usually filled with water (solvent) and various solutes. Water and solutes also make up the external medium surrounding cells. What separates the inside from the outside is, of course, the cell membrane. The cell membrane acts as a barrier to the free movement of most polar solutes into or out of cells. Some solutes obviously do pass through membranes either on their own or with the help of transport proteins. Whether a molecule passes through a membrane or not depends on 1) its physical properties, 2) the existence of

Adapted from *Bio 214 Laboratory Investigations in Cell and Molecular Biology*, 2008–2009 ed., by Jonathan Monroe as modified by Ilya Tëmkin. Copyright © 2009 by Hayden-McNeil, LLC. Additional duplication is prohibited without written permission of Hayden-McNeil, LLC.

transport proteins in the membrane, and 3) whether there is a force driving its movement. *Both a driving force and the capacity for movement are necessary for a molecule to pass through a membrane.* If a molecule is capable of crossing a membrane but no concentration gradient exists, there will be no net movement. If a molecule is incapable of crossing a membrane, it will not cross even if a steep concentration gradient exists.

Driving forces can act on both solutes and the solvent, water. When considering membrane transport recall that solutes tend to move by **diffusion** down their concentration and/or electrical (if the solute is an ion) gradient towards equilibrium. Similarly, water also moves down its concentration gradient by **osmosis** from regions of more water (less solutes) to regions of less water (more solutes). What is important in determining the direction of water movement across a membrane is the relative concentration of solutes inside and outside of the cell. When the outside solution has fewer solutes than the cell, the outside solution is said to be **hypotonic**. In a hypotonic solution, solutes will tend to move out of the cell down their concentration gradient if they can, but water will tend to move into the cell down its concentration gradient. When there are more solutes outside a cell than inside, the outside is **hypertonic** and water will move out of the cell. When the solute concentrations inside and outside are identical the outside solution is **isotonic** to the cell. When *Paramecia*, single-celled freshwater organisms, are placed in a hypotonic solution (H_2O), water moves in by osmosis and is pumped back out using the contractile vacuoles in order to prevent the cells from expanding. Also, the rate of contractile vacuole pumping is faster when the osmotic gradient across the cell is larger. For many years it was puzzling that water, a highly polar substance, could cross the hydrophobic interior of membranes as easily as it does! We now know that membranes that are permeable to water contain water-selective protein channels called aquaporins.

Osmolarity is a term used to express a solution's total concentration of osmotically active solute particles. Recall that molarity expresses the number of moles of a certain substance per liter of solution, and that a mole consists of Avogadro's number of molecules. Similarly, osmolarity expresses the number of moles of all solute particles per liter of solution. For example, a 1.0 osmolar (osM) solution contains 1.0 mole of solute particles per liter. However, unlike molarity, which refers to a single molecular species, osmolarity may be used to express the concentration of a mixture of various molecules in solution. The osmolarity of a solution having only one solute that does not ionize (e.g., glucose) is equal to the molarity of the solution because the molecules do not dissociate into ions in solution and each molecule is a solute particle. Electrolytes dissociate into ions when in solution, yielding more than Avogadro's number of solute particles per mole of the original compound. Ideally, a mole of NaCl in solution would yield two moles of solute particles (ions). However, at higher concentrations ions interact by electrostatic attraction thereby decreasing the number of solute particles in the solution. For this lab exercise we will ignore this complication.

Activity 1: Observation of Plasmolysis Using *Elodea*

MATERIALS

- Compound microscope
- Lens paper
- Lens cleaning solution
- Sucrose solutions (0.2 M, 0.3 M, 0.4 M, 0.5 M, 0.6 M)
- Paper towels or Kimwipes
- Living *Elodea*
- Slides
- Coverslips
- 5-50 µL or 10-100 µL pipetters
- Pipette tips

PROCEDURE

1. Working in pairs, make a wet mount of an *Elodea* leaf in deionized (dH_2O) water and observe it under the microscope using the 40× objective lens. Draw a diagram of several cells in Box 4-1. Label all parts of the cells that you can see.

   You should be able to see green chloroplasts randomly distributed in the cytoplasm of each cell. In the case of cells such as these that possess cell walls, the term **protoplast** is used for that part of the cell within and including the plasma membrane. When the leaf is in water (hypotonic), the protoplast of each cell is fully expanded and pressed tightly against the cell wall and the cell appears "plump" or **turgid**. As in bacteria and fungi, plant cell walls prevent the protoplast from bursting when cells are placed in a hypotonic solution. Most of each protoplast's volume is a central vacuole filled with fluid and confined by the **tonoplast**, or vacuolar membrane. Plant vacuoles are not contractile. The remainder of the cytoplasm, with its conspicuous chloroplasts and other less apparent organelles, is restricted to a thin outer layer between the tonoplast and the plasma membrane. You cannot see the tonoplast or the plasma membrane with a light microscope. The cell wall, which is produced by the protoplast, is a porous, relatively rigid structure composed of cellulose, several other polysaccharides, and proteins.

2. Prepare wet mounts of individual *Elodea* leaves in 0.2, 0.3, 0.4, 0.5, and 0.6 M sucrose solutions. For each wet mount, remove a healthy leaf from a sprig, place the leaf on a clean slide with the upper leaf surface facing up, drain the excess water with a Kimwipe or a paper towel, and add 50 µL of the sucrose solution and a coverslip. Several wet mounts can be prepared simultaneously. As the osmolarity of the external solution increases (becomes hypertonic), water will begin to leave the cells and the protoplasts will shrink away from the cell wall. This process is called **plasmolysis**. *Don't confuse this term describing plant cells that have lost water*

with hemolysis that describes red blood cells that have gained water and burst. Begin by examining the leaves in 0.6 M sucrose to more easily see what plasmolysis looks like.

3. Describe the changes in the cells in Table 4-1 as you examine each preparation for about 5 minutes. Notice that the extent of plasmolysis in increasingly hypertonic concentrations is progressive. While plasmolysis will be visible in some of the solutions, you will not see any difference between cells that are in an isotonic solution with those that are turgid in a hypotonic solution. The isotonic solution will therefore be the one with the highest solute concentration in which the cells are not plasmolyzed.

4. Record the osmolarity for each solution of sucrose. What solution is isotonic to these *Elodea* cells? What is the apparent osmolarity of these *Elodea* cells?

OSMOSIS AND DIFFUSION:
Activity 1

Name

Date

Section

Box 4-1.

Table 4-1. *Observations of* Elodea *cells exposed to various concentrations of sucrose.*

Sucrose (M)	Observations of *Elodea* Cells (Drawings and Notes)	Tonicity
0	from previous page	hypotonic
0.2		
0.3		
0.4		
0.5		
0.6		hypertonic

Activity 2: Observations of Hemolysis and Crenation Using Sheep Erythrocytes

Erythrocytes, the chief cellular component of blood, number nearly six million per cubic millimeter of human blood. The main function of the pigment hemoglobin, from which erythrocytes derive their red color, is to transport oxygen from the gas exchange surface (gills, lungs, etc.) to the tissues. Hemoglobin also helps carry a waste product, carbon dioxide (CO_2), from the tissues to the respiratory surfaces for excretion. The erythrocytes of all mammals have become so extremely specialized for oxygen transport that they lose their nuclei at maturity. This permits maximum hemoglobin content per cell. Their shape is a biconcave disc that is 8 micrometers in diameter.

Because animal cells lack a cell wall, they are very sensitive to their osmotic environment. When an erythrocyte is placed in a **hypertonic** medium (more solutes outside than inside), it shrinks and assumes the shape of a sphere with small spikes on its surface. The shrinking of red blood cells is called **crenation**. On the other hand, when erythrocytes are placed in a **hypotonic** medium (fewer solutes outside than inside), the cell swells. If it swells beyond the capacity of the membrane to expand, the membrane ruptures and releases hemoglobin. **Hemolysis** is the rupturing of erythrocytes and the consequential escape of hemoglobin from the cell.

MATERIALS

+ Compound microscope
+ Lens paper
+ Lens cleaning solution
+ NaCL solutions (0.05 M, 0.15 M, 0.6 M, Unknown M)
+ Paper towels or Kimwipes
+ Whole sheep blood
+ Slides
+ Coverslips
+ 2-20 µL and 5-50 µL pipetters
+ Pipette tips
+ Eppendorf tubes

PROCEDURE

1. Working in *pairs*, place 1 mL of the following solutions in four labeled Eppendorf tubes: 0.15 M NaCl, 0.6 M NaCl, 0.05 M NaCl, and the unknown solution of NaCl.

2. Add 40 µL of whole sheep blood to the 0.15 M NaCl, close cap, and invert twice to mix the solution.

3. Place 10 µL of the dilute suspension on a microscope slide and cover with a coverslip. Examine the cells at 40× magnification. If you have trouble finding the cells, focus on the edge of the coverslip first. Note the appearance of the cells when they are lying flat on the glass slide. **The preparation must be examined immediately**, since erythrocytes in a wet mount soon change their shape. Draw what you see in Table 4-2.

4. Repeat the procedure outlined in steps 2 and 3, using each of the remaining NaCl solutions.

5. Examine the cells for several minutes looking for signs of crenation or hemolysis and record your observations in Table 4-2. In the hypotonic solution, hemolysis will occur very quickly and the resulting empty membranes or "ghosts" will be extremely difficult to see, especially at high light levels, so close down the sub stage iris and use high magnification. Don't be discouraged if you can't see them.

6. Record the osmolarity for each known solution of NaCl. Recall that osmolarity is not always equal to molarity. What is the approximate **osmolarity** of these erythrocytes?

7. Is the unknown solution hypotonic, isotonic, or hypertonic compared with red blood cells?

8. Lastly, hold the four test tubes in front of a piece of paper with text printed on it. Can you read the text through any of the tubes? This is, in fact, a very simple way to observe hemolysis.

You can determine that hemolysis has occurred by holding a test tube containing a suspension of red blood cells against a white page with printed black text. Red blood cells are translucent but will not allow you to read the text CLEARLY through the tube. When approximately 75% of the cells have hemolyzed, the suspension will become transparent and you will easily be able to see the text through the tube. It is at this point that you will record the time of hemolysis in the following experiment.

OSMOSIS AND DIFFUSION:
Activity 2

Name _____

Date _____

Section _____

Table 4-2. *Observations of sheep erythrocytes exposed to various concentrations of NaCl.*

NaCl (M)	Observations of Erythrocytes (Drawings and Notes)	Tonicity
0.15		isotonic
0.60		hypertonic
0.05		hypotonic
X		———

1. Define plasmolysis.

2. Explain why erythrocytes hemolyze when exposed to a hypertonic solution of a compound that is highly lipid soluble.

5

Enzymes

OBJECTIVES

After completing this lab, you should be able to:

+ Name the components of an enzymatic reaction.

+ Describe the function of enzymes.

+ Graph data, analyze results, and draw conclusions.

+ Explain how concentrations of enzymes and substrates, and environmental conditions, affect the rate of chemical reactions.

INTRODUCTION

Chemical reactions occur when bonds are broken and bonds are formed **with or without enzymes present**. A set amount of energy needs to be put in to begin a chemical reaction. More energy may be released as products form (energy out = **catabolic**) than the initial energy put in, or less energy may be released as the products form (net energy input = **anabolic**) than the initial energy put in to begin the reaction.

When enzymes participate in a chemical reaction, it acts as a **catalyst** because it **increases the rate of a reaction**. That is, more products to form in a set amount of time than when the enzyme is not present. Recall that an enzyme can only increase the rate of a reaction; it cannot cause a reaction to occur which will not occur when the enzyme is absent. The rate of chemical reaction cannot be increased if the wrong enzyme is used. In the same way, your car key will not unlock the door to your home.

Most enzymes are proteins which will form their correct 3-D shape, or **conformation**, due to the order of the amino acids present. The shape makes an **active site** on the enzyme, a place where the reactant fits precisely.

In a chemical reaction, a certain amount of energy is needed to initially break bonds, so new bonds can form; this energy is called **activation energy**. Enzymes lower the energy needed to begin a chemical reaction because the reactants are held in an orientation that favors the breaking old bonds and forming new bonds.

Adapted from *BIO 103 Introductory Biology*, copyright © 2012 by David Luther as modified by the Department of Biology, Northern Virginia Community College, Annandale Campus. Additional duplication is prohibited without written permission of Hayden-McNeil, LLC and David Luther.

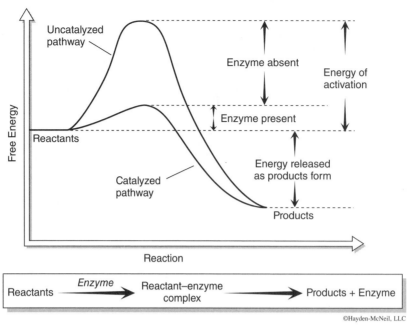

Figure 5-1. *Free energy of a chemical reaction.*

When an **inhibitor** (blocker) sits in the enzyme's active site, it cannot work as a catalyst. Many **factors** can change the shape of an enzyme and cause it to not work: some factors that change a protein's 3-D shape are heat and chemicals.

A small increase in temperature can **increase** how fast an enzyme catalyzes a reaction because the molecules will collide into each other more often. But increasing the **temperature** of a protein too much changes the shape, permanently. (It is unfolded or "denatured.") Likewise, adding too much **acid** or too much **base** will change the pH and that can unfold a protein, changing or blocking the active site. Two additional small molecules, called **cofactors** (elements from the periodic tables) or **coenzymes** (from vitamins) can assist enzymes in doing their work. The cofactors can also be critical to hold the protein into its correct 3-D shape.

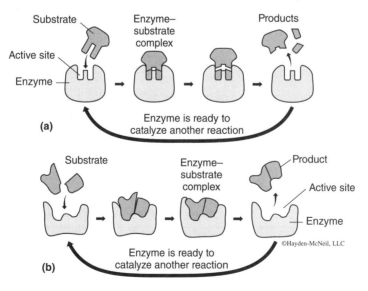

Figure 5-2. *Enzymes are specific and recycled.*

The reaction you will test today (equation 1) involves molecules present in potatoes. Did you ever see a potato turn brown when it has been cut and left on the counter? The brown molecule is **benzoquinone** or simply quinone; it forms from the reactant **catechol** in the presence of oxygen. The enzyme that speeds up this chemical reaction is called **catecholase**, and is also found in potatoes. The enzyme's name helps you remember it is **specific** for its correct **substrate** (reactant) catechol.

The reaction is a "redox" reaction because it involves a pair of reactions. Reduction reactions occur when an electron (or H atom) is gained. Oxidation reactions occur when an electron (or a H atom) is lost. Many biological reactions involve loss and gain of the entire H atom. In equation 1 the reactant, catechol, loses two H atoms, and forms the oxidized product, quinone. At the same time the reactant, oxygen, gains the 2 H atoms to form the reduced product, water.

+ Do you think this reaction can be reversed?

+ Predict what you could do to observe when the reaction is reversed.

Equation 1

$$Catechol \quad + \quad \tfrac{1}{2}O_2 \quad \xrightarrow{Catecholase} \quad Benzoquinone \quad + \quad H_2O$$

We can write this reaction in a simplified way: (where E= enzyme, S = substrate, P = product) showing that the enzyme participates in the reaction temporarily, but it is not consumed. It is unchanged when the reaction ends.

$$S + E \rightarrow [ES] \rightarrow [EP] \rightarrow P + E$$

The equation shows that the overall reaction involves **converting** the substrate, S, to the product, P. The middle steps, in brackets [ES] and [EP], show that the reaction uses the enzyme temporarily, but the enzyme, E, is released unchanged at the end. Therefore, the enzyme is available to work again and help convert another molecule of substrate into another molecule of product.

Stop and think.

+ If there are 500 molecules of **S** and 5 molecules of **E**, will all of the substrate S get changed to product P?

+ If there are 500 molecules of **S** and 50 molecules of **E**, will the reaction still work at the same rate as in the first condition?

+ If there are 500 molecules of **S** and 5000 molecules of **E**, what can you predict?

As noted in equation 1, catechol is oxidized by the enzyme to form quinone. Quinone is then converted through a series of spontaneous reactions to produce a heterogeneous group of polymers called **melanins**. As the polymers gets larger, their colors deepen from pink-gold through orange-brown and finally to an intense brown-black color. The larger molecules are less soluble in water, so eventually they precipitate from the solution.

By observing the product yield during a set amount of time, the rate of the reaction (equation 1) is measured. Your data will be *qualitative*. Rank as: 0, +, ++, +++, ++++.

SERIAL DILUTION

For some of the activities in this lab you will be testing the effect of varying concentration of different solutions. To prepare solutions of different concentration you will use a technique called serial dilution. A serial dilution is the stepwise dilution of a substance, usually using the same dilution factor at each step (Figure 5-3). For example, a ten-fold serial dilution could be 1 M, 0.1 M, 0.01 M, 0.001 M.

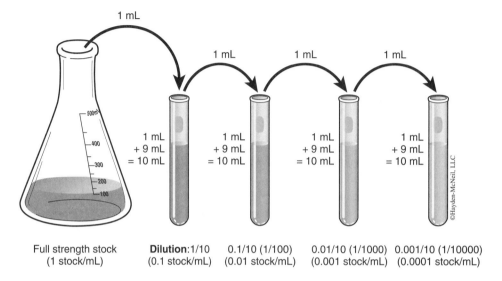

Figure 5-3.

Materials

+ Catechol stock solution
+ Catecholase stock solution (keep on ice)
+ Distilled water
+ Buffers at pH 2, 4, 6, 7, 8, 10, 12
+ Thermometers
+ 10 mL graduated cylinders
+ Test tubes on a rack
+ 400 mL beakers
+ Disposable pipettes
+ Water bath
+ Parafilm
+ Scissors
+ Sharpie marker

CAUTION: Catechol, hydroxyquinone, and phenylthiourea (PTU) are hazardous if ingested or absorbed through the skin. If you are using these materials please wear plastic gloves when you handle the chemicals. If an accident occurs, immediately wash your hands thoroughly with warm water and soap.

Activity 1: Effect of Temperature

PROCEDURE

1. Label test tubes A1, A2, A3, A4, A5, A6, and place 3 mL of each of the following solutions into the respective tubes. Each test tube will contain a total volume of 6 mL. Why is that important?

Table 5-1.

Tube #	Catechol (mL)	H_2O (mL)	Catecholase (mL)	Total Volume (mL)
A1	3	–	3	6
A2	–	3	3	6
A3	3	3	–	6
A4	3	–	3	6
A5	–	3	3	6
A6	3	3	–	6

2. Cover the tubes with Parafilm and gently invert them to mix contents.

3. Record the color intensity of each solution in Table 5-2. Rank color as 0, +, ++, +++, ++++.

4. Keep three test tubes—A1, A2, and A3—in 21 °C on the bench for 15 minutes.

5. Place three test tubes—A4, A5, and A6—in a 40 °C water bath for 15 minutes.

6. Agitate the solutions and record the color intensity in Table 5-2 at 5-minute intervals.

7. At the end of the 15 minutes, remove the test tubes from the water bath. Keep the tubes for color comparisons in later experiments.

Save the tubes for color comparisons in later exercises.

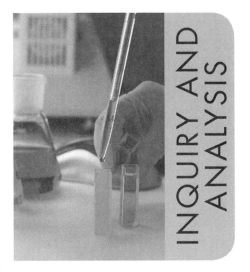

INQUIRY AND ANALYSIS

ENZYMES: Activity 1

Name _____

Date _____

Section _____

1. What is the rate of the conversion of catechol to quinone by catecholase?

    Write a hypothesis to predict how quickly the brown product, quinone, is formed at room temperature.

    Hypothesis:

2. What is the effect of an increased temperature on the rate of the conversion?

    Write a hypothesis to test the differences in temperature on the reaction rate.

    Hypothesis:

Table 5-2.

21 °C		Time (in Minutes)			
Test Tube	Contents	0	5	10	15
A1					
A2					
A3					

40 °C		Time (in Minutes)			
Test Tube	Contents	0	5	10	15
A4					
A5					
A6					

3. Describe the time it took to see the product at 21 °C.

4. Describe the differences in product yield at the two temperatures.

5. Did you support or not support your two hypotheses?

Activity 2: Effect of Enzyme Concentration

How does enzyme concentration affect enzyme activity? You can vary the enzyme's concentration by diluting it with a pH 7 buffer solution. A buffer solution resists any change in pH by releasing or taking up hydrogen ions (H^+).

PROCEDURE

1. Label test tubes B1, B2, B3, and B4, and place 3 mL of the substrate (catechol) in each tube.

2. Prepare ten-fold serial dilution of the enzyme (catecholase) and add the 3 mL of the diluted enzyme to the tubes B1–B4 as shown in Table 5-3.

Table 5-3.

Tube #	Catechol mL	H₂O mL	Catecholase mL	Total Volume mL
B1	3	–	3 (stock)	6
B2	3	-	3 (1:10)	6
B3	3	-	3 (1:100)	6
B4	3	–	3 (1:1000)	6

3. Once you have made your solutions and *noted the initial color intensities*, place the tubes in the 40 °C water bath for 15 minutes. **Always keep catecholase on ice!**

4. Agitate the tubes every 5 minutes, and record the resulting color intensities. Rank color as 0, +, ++, +++, ++++.

5. Record your results and conclusions; use Table 5-4.

6. Graph the results. Include a title and label the axes.

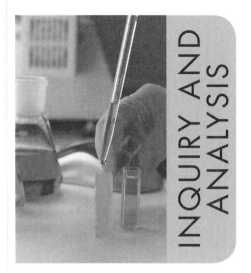

INQUIRY AND ANALYSIS

ENZYMES: Activity 2

Name

Date

Section

1. Record your hypothesis:

Table 5-4.

Test Tube	Concentration	Time (in Minutes)			
		0	5	10	15
B1					
B2					
B3					
B4					

Product Yield vs. Enzyme Concentration

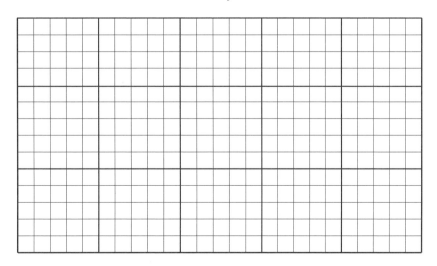

2. Describe the effect that varying the enzyme concentration has on rate of product formation.

3. Did you support or not support your hypotheses?

Activity 3: Effect of Substrate Concentration

How does substrate concentration affect enzyme activity? That is, if you keep the amount of enzyme constant, how will the enzymatic activity change as you add more and more substrate?

PROCEDURE

1. Label test tubes C1, C2, C3, C4, C5, and place 3 mL of the enzyme (catecholase) stock solution in each tube.

2. Prepare ten-fold serial dilution of the substrate (catechol) and add the 3 mL of the diluted substrate to the tubes C1–C5 as shown in Table 5-5.

Table 5-5.

Tube #	Catechol mL	H_2O mL	Catecholase mL	Total Volume mL
C1	3 (stock)	–	3	6
C2	3 (1:10)	–	3	6
C3	3 (1:100)	–	3	6
C4	3 (1:1000)	–	3	6
C5	3 (1:10000)	–	3	6

3. Record the initial color intensities for all the solutions and place the test tubes in the 40° water bath for 15 minutes.

4. Agitate the tubes every 5 minutes, and note their color intensities. Rank color as 0, +, ++, +++, ++++.

5. Record your results and conclusions in Table 5-6.

6. Graph the results. Include a title and label the axes.

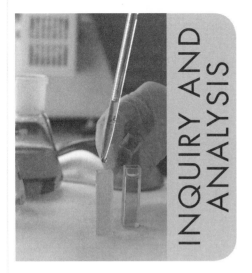

ENZYMES: Activity 3

Name _____

Date _____

Section _____

1. Record your hypothesis:

Table 5-6.

Test Tube	Concentration	Time (in Minutes)			
		0	5	10	15
C1					
C2					
C3					
C4					
C5					

Product Yield vs. Substrate Concentration

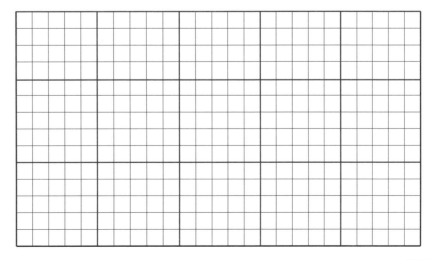

2. Describe the effect that varying the substrate concentration has on rate of product formation.

3. Did you support or not support your hypotheses?

Activity 4: Effect of pH

How does pH affect the activity of enzymes? Many of the chemical bonds that hold a protein in its three-dimensional shape are affected by the presence of hydrogen ions (H^+). The buffer solutions in the series you will use in this exercise vary in pH. By exposing the enzyme–substrate complex to a range of pH values, you can test the effect of hydrogen ion concentration on enzymatic activity.

PROCEDURE

1. Label eight test tubes D1–D8 and place 2 mL of the substrate (catechol) in seven tubes, D2–D8.

2. To each tube add buffer and the enzyme (catecholase) as shown in Table 5-7.

Table 5-7.

Tube #	Undiluted Catechol, mL	Volume of buffer, mL	Undiluted Catecholase, mL
D1	0	4 mL pH 7	2
D2	2	2 mL pH 2	2
D3	2	2 ml pH 4	2
D4	2	2 mL pH 6	2
D5	2	2 mL pH 7	2
D6	2	2 mL pH 8	2
D7	2	2 mL pH 10	2
D8	2	2 mL pH 12	2

3. Record the initial color intensities for all the solutions and place the test tubes in the 40° water bath for 15 minutes.

4. Agitate the tubes every 5 minutes, and note their color intensities. Rank color as 0, +, ++, +++, ++++.

5. Record your results and conclusions in Table 5-8.

6. Graph the results. Include a title and label the axes.

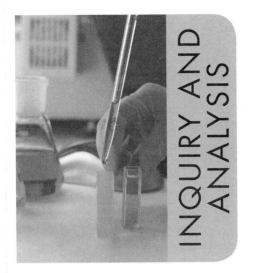

INQUIRY AND ANALYSIS

ENZYMES: Activity 4

_____

Name

_____

Date

_____

Section

1. Record your hypothesis:

Table 5-8.

Test Tube	pH	Time (in Minutes)			
		0	5	10	15
D1					
D2					
D3					
D4					
D5					
D6					
D7					
D8					

Product Yield vs. pH

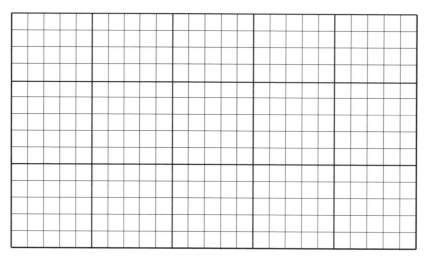

2. Describe the effect that varying the substrate concentration has on rate of product formation.

3. Did you support or not support your hypotheses?

4. Describe the results obtained and what they mean.

5. Note any trends or changes in trends.

6. What potential sources of error may have altered your results?

7. How could you avoid those errors if you repeated this experiment?

8. Evaluate your hypotheses overall. Summarize your main findings.

OBJECTIVES

After completing this lab, you should be able to:

+ Describe how to demonstrate carbon dioxide and ethanol production during fermentation.

+ List the requirements for anaerobic fermentation.

+ List the requirements for the Krebs cycle reaction in which succinate is transformed to fumarate.

+ Describe how the electron transport chain works in aerobic respiration.

+ Explain how the indicator TTC (2,3,5-triphenyl tetrazolium chloride) can be used to determine whether seeds are viable.

INTRODUCTION

Many metabolic reactions within the cell do not occur spontaneously but require a source of chemical energy in the form of ATP (adenosine triphosphate). The major source of ATP for most cells is the oxidation of glucose, a series of enzymatic reactions that results in the breakdown of carbon compounds into carbon dioxide, water, and energy.

The oxidation of glucose takes place in two major stages (Figure 6-1). The first is **glycolysis**, an **anaerobic** process (one that can proceed in the absence of oxygen).

Adapted from *Biology in the Laboratory*, 3rd ed., by Doris R. Helms, Carl W. Helms, Robert J. Kosinski, and John R. Cummings as modified by Ilya Tëmkin. Copyright © 1998 by W.H. Freeman and Company. Additional duplication is prohibited without written permission of W.H. Freeman and Company.

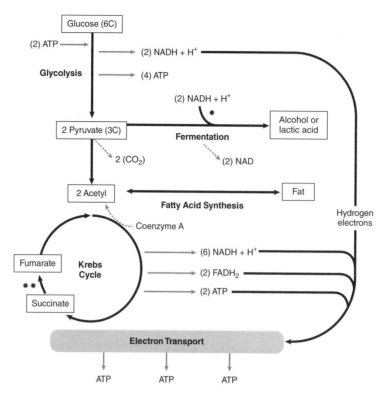

Figure 6-1. *Overview of cellular respiration.*

Glycolysis occurs in the cytoplasm of both **aerobic** (oxygen-requiring) and anaerobic organisms. The end product of glycolysis is pyruvic acid.

When oxygen is unavailable, the conversion of glucose to pyruvic acid is the major source of energy. In some organisms, such as yeasts, pyruvic acid can be further metabolized by a second series of reactions, the anaerobic process of **fermentation**, which results in the production of alcohol and carbon dioxide. Lactic acid can also be formed by the anaerobic metabolism of pyruvic acid. For example, when the oxygen supply available to muscle cells is depleted during strenuous exercise, lactic acid is produced. Eventually, as oxygen becomes available, lactic acid is used to resynthesize pyruvate.

When oxygen is available, the second stage in the oxidation of glucose is aerobic cellular respiration, which consists of the Krebs cycle (or *citric acid cycle*) and electron transport. These reactions, which take place in the mitochondria, greatly increase the energy harvest from the oxidation of glucose.

During this laboratory, you will study the processes of fermentation and respiration by making observations about the products of cellular reactions.

Activity 1: Production of Carbon Dioxide and Ethanol by Fermentation

Yeasts are simple unicellular organisms related to mushrooms, molds, and mildews. They are called **heterotrophs** because they do not carry out photosynthesis, but obtain their food from outside sources such as grapes or grain. Yeasts are also classified as **facultative anaerobes**—they can live in aerobic or anaerobic environments. Under anaerobic conditions, yeasts carry out fermentation to produce alcohol and carbon dioxide. The alcohol in wine, beer, and other beverages is produced by the metabolic reactions of yeasts grown on grapes and grains such as barley.

$$C_6H_{12}O_6 \rightarrow 2C_2H_5OH + 2CO_2 + \text{energy}$$
$$\text{glucose} \qquad \text{ethanol} \quad \text{carbon} \atop \text{dioxide}$$

Very little net energy is produced during the process of fermentation—only two ATPs for every glucose molecule metabolized—but this is sufficient to sustain existing yeast cells.

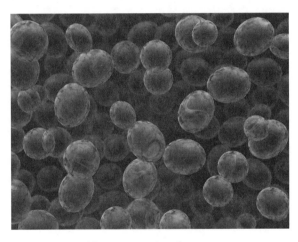

Figure 6-2. *Budding yeast,* Saccharomyces cerevisiae.

MATERIALS

+ 4 fermenting vials (4 large + 4 small tubes)
+ Living yeast solution
+ Boiled yeast solution
+ 5% glucose solution
+ 5% sucrose solution
+ Distilled water
+ Pipettes and pipettor
+ 10 mL graduated cylinder

Requirements for Fermentation in Yeast

In this experiment, the class will study the role of yeasts as well as the food source requirements for fermentation. You will be assigned to one of four treatment groups by your laboratory instructor (Table 6-1).

Table 6-1.

Treatment	Yeast	Boiled Yeast	Sugar	Water
I	10 mL	–	5% glucose	–
II	10 mL	–	5% sucrose	–
III	–	10 mL	5% glucose	–
IV	10 mL	–	–	Distilled water

PROCEDURE

1. In each assigned laboratory group, work in pairs. Obtain two fermenting vials, one large and one small.

2. Add 10 mL of yeast suspension (boiled yeast suspension if you are assigned to Group III) to the smaller vial.

3. Finish filling the small vial to its brim with the sugar solution or with distilled water, as designated for your group.

4. Hold the small vial upright. Invert the large vial so that the bottom side is upward and lower it to cover the small vial.

5. Hold the two vials tightly together at their ends and invert the apparatus so that the small vial is now upside down within the larger vial (Figure 6-3). As CO_2 is produced by the process of fermentation, it will collect in the upper portion of the small vial and the yeast mixture will be pushed downward and out into the larger vial.

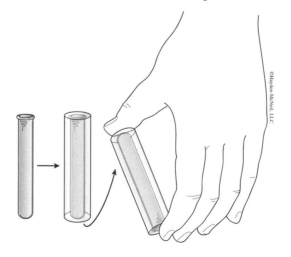

Figure 6-3. *Fermentation apparatus.*

6. If there is an air space at the top of the small vial, measure its length using a millimeter ruler and use this measurement as the zero point.

7. Measure the length of the gas column at 5-minute intervals for as long as possible (up to 45 minutes). Foaming within the large vial may obscure the length of the gas column. If you find it difficult to read, move the small vial until its side is pressed against the side of the outer vial.

8. Record your readings in Table 6-2, and remember to subtract the value for the zero point from each reading.

9. Record the data for all teams (student pairs) in your group. Average the data for each time period and place all group data on the blackboard.

10. Copy the class data for other groups into Table 6-2 and plot the data (using the averages) on graph paper. Always graph dependent variables along the vertical (Y) axis; in this case, "gas column (mm)"; "time (min)" should be plotted on the horizontal (X) axis. Be sure to label your graph. Use either colored pencils or different symbols to designate the four different groups.

11. Since the vials are uniform cylinders, the rate of increase in the length of the space filled by CO_2 is directly proportional to the rate of CO_2 production. To determine the actual rate, pick any two points on the straight-line portion of the curve (or a straight line approximated to the curve). Divide the difference in the gas column height (in millimeters) between the two points by the difference in time between the two points. The result will be the rate of CO_2 production in millimeters per minute.

Millimeters can be converted to volume (milliliters) by using the formula for the volume (V) of a cylinder, $\pi r^2 h = V$, where r is the radius of the cylinder (in millimeters) and h is the height of the gas column (in millimeters). This will allow fermentation rates to be expressed as milliliters per minute. Record fermentation rates in Table 6-3.

INQUIRY AND ANALYSIS

Name _____

Date _____

Section _____

During the processes of glycolysis and fermentation, yeasts use sugars, but not all sugars are used at the same rate. Why do you think this might happen? Can you formulate a hypothesis about the requirements that must be met in order to maximize the rate of fermentation?

Hypothesis:

1. What do you **predict** will happen in the experiment (consider all treatments)?

2. What do you predict will happen in your treatment compared with other treatments?

3. What is the **independent variable** in this experiment?

4. What is the **dependent variable** in this experiment?

5. Now measure the fermentation rates for the four treatments.

Table 6-2. *Class data for yeast fermentation experiment, recorded as length of gas column (in millimeters).*

Minutes	Group 1 Treatment:	Group 2 Treatment:	Group 3 Treatment:	Group 4 Treatment:	Group 5 Treatment:	Group 6 Treatment:	Group 7 Treatment:
0							
5							
10							
15							
20							
25							
30							
35							
40							
45							

Table 6-3.

Treatment Group	Fermentation Rate (mL/min)
I	
II	
III	
IV	

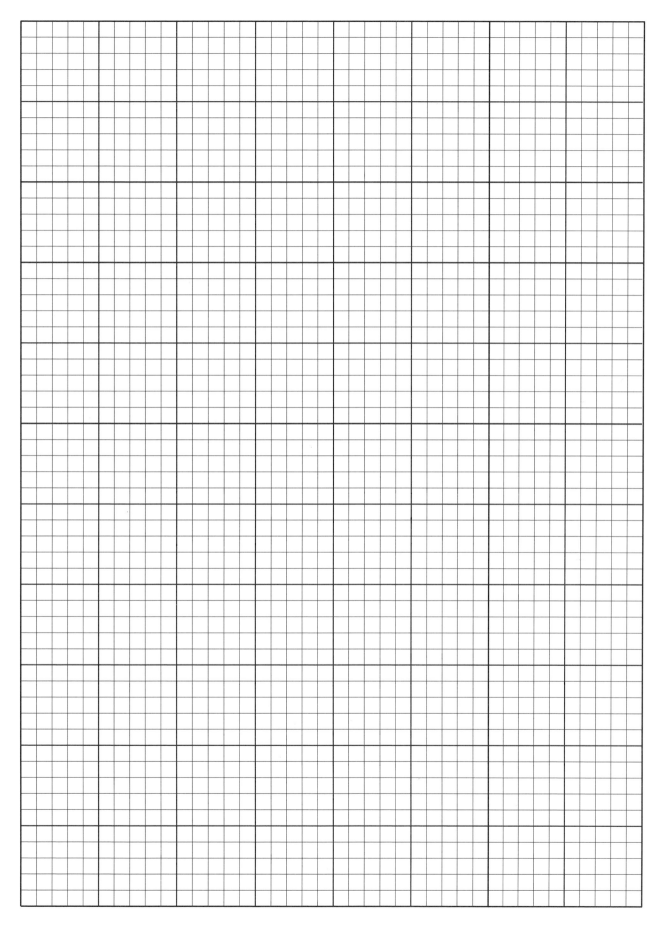

6. What do the data from each group tell you about the process of fermentation?

Group I

Group II

Group III

Group IV

7. Why was Group IV included in this experiment?

8. What is the effect of boiling the yeast (Group III)?

9. Group III serves as a control for this experiment. What other setup could be included as a control for this experiment?

10. Do your results support your hypothesis?

11. Your null hypothesis?

12. What do you **conclude** about the role of yeasts in the process of fermentation?

13. What do you conclude about the importance of the type of sugar used as a food source for yeasts in the process of fermentation?

Activity 2: Respiration in Plant Embryos

Several tests are used by the agricultural industry to check the viability of seeds before planting. One of these tests involves the use of the dye tetrazolium, which is colorless when oxidized but becomes reddish when reduced. The test relies on whether or not the seed's electron transport system is working. When tetrazolium is added to a living cell, it will interact with the electron transport system to accept hydrogen electrons as they are transferred from the cytochromes. When tetrazolium accepts these electrons, it is reduced and turns red or a deep pink. If the seed is dead, the electron transport system will not be functioning, no hydrogens will be available to reduce the tetrazolium, and the seed will remain colorless.

MATERIALS

+ 3 living bean seeds or 3 living corn seeds

+ 3 dead bean seeds or 3 dead corn seeds

+ 2 Petri/weigh dishes

+ Scalpels

+ TTC solution

PROCEDURE

1. On the demonstration table you will find two groups (A and B) of seeds (beans or corn). One lot has been boiled and is dead. The other is alive. Test the two groups of seeds for viability. Cut three seeds from each group in half along their long axis with a sharp razor blade (Figure 6-4).

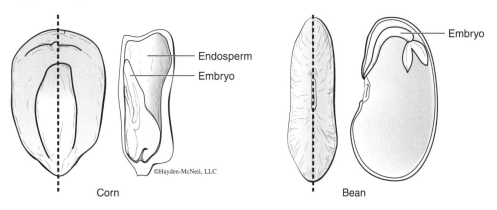

Corn   Bean

©Hayden-McNeil, LLC

Figure 6-4. *Seeds cut to show embryo.*

2. Compare your cross section of the seed with that shown in Figure 6-4 to be sure that you have exposed the embryo. Locate the embryo, endosperm (food for the growing seed), and seed coat of your seeds.

    a. Which tissue would you expect to stain red after application of the TTC reagent?

3. Place several drops of TTC into two Petri dishes. Label one Petri dish for the A group of seeds and another for the B group. Place the seed halves with their cut side down in the Petri dishes; add enough TTC to completely cover the seeds.

    Caution: TTC is a poison; avoid contact with skin. Wash immediately if you come into direct contact with TTC.

4. At the end of the laboratory period, turn the seed halves over and examine them. Use forceps!

    Which group of seeds is alive and respiring?

    How do you know?

5. Cyanide affects the electron transport system by binding to components of the system (the cytochromes), thereby inhibiting the transfer of electrons.

    If seeds were treated with cyanide, what results would they show in the tetrazolium test?

    Explain.

RESPIRATION: Activity 2

Name _____

Date _____

Section _____

1. Where in the cell do the following processes occur?

    glycolysis

    fermentation

    Krebs cycle

    electron transport

2. Why is fermentation considered to be an inefficient process?

3. Why is the process of fermentation called anaerobic?

4. Complete the following chart.

	Requirements	Products	Final Electron Acceptor
Alcoholic Fermentation			
Lactic Acid Fermentation			
Aerobic Respiration			

5. You have just finished running a 3-minute mile. Your legs are cramping badly and you are breathing very rapidly. How could heavy breathing be beneficial?

6. Ten glucose molecules are broken down during glycolysis. How many pyruvate molecules are produced?

Each of the 3-carbon pyruvate molecules can yield a 2-carbon acetyl fragment after CO_2 is removed. How many acetyl compounds can be produced from the 10 glucose molecules?

If these are used to produce a fatty acid, how many carbons would be in the fatty acid chain?

Draw the fatty acid in the space below.

7. A farmer has a large bag of pea seeds left over from last year's planting. He would like to save some money by planting the seeds, but is not sure that a sufficient percentage of the seeds remains viable. How could he determine what percentage of the seeds would be expected to germinate?

OBJECTIVES

After completing this lab, you should be able to:

+ Explain the role of pigments in photosynthesis.

+ Conduct chromatography and spectrophotometry analyses.

INTRODUCTION

What do you think of when you picture a solar collector? Something silver, or dark black and shiny? Perhaps you remember the small rectangles above the LCD screen of your calculator, or an odd contraption on the roof of a neighbor's house? The first man-made solar cells were produced in the 1950s, and like modern solar cells they used energy from sunlight to create an electric current. The Earth, however, has had natural solar collectors for at least 3 billion years, in the form of a bright green pigment named **chlorophyll** (Figure 7-1). Just like man-made solar cells, chlorophyll collects solar energy and ultimately releases a controlled flow of electrons (electricity!) that plants use for energy.

Deep within each plant cell, we find tens or sometimes hundreds of bright green chloroplasts—the *organelle that houses photosynthesis* (Figure 7-1). The chloroplasts are green because of *tiny, stacked membrane sacs* called **thylakoids**, which house thousands of chlorophyll molecules that absorb sunlight. Eventually, the energy they absorb is enough to start electrons flowing within the thylakoid membrane—very much like electricity! Those moving electrons provide enough energy to form oxygen and ATP within the chloroplasts. These steps are called the **"light reactions"** of photosynthesis, since they depend on sunlight.

ATP is the *energy-carrying molecule* in all living things. Plants use ATP (formed during the light reactions) to *build sugar out of carbon dioxide molecules*. This process is called the **Calvin cycle**. It occurs in the stroma, the fluid space around the thylakoids. (The Calvin cycle is sometimes called the "dark reactions" of photosynthesis, because it can occur without light as long as ATP is present.)

Adapted from *Biology 104 Laboratory Manual*, 3rd ed., by the West Virginia University Board of Governors as modified by Ilya Tëmkin. Copyright © 2009 by Hayden-McNeil, LLC. Additional duplication is prohibited without written permission of Hayden-McNeil, LLC.

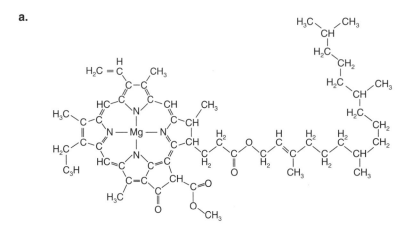

a.

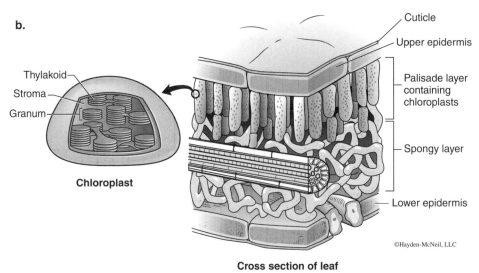

b.

Cuticle

Upper epidermis

Palisade layer containing chloroplasts

Spongy layer

Lower epidermis

Thylakoid

Stroma

Granum

Chloroplast

©Hayden-McNeil, LLC

Cross section of leaf

Figure 7-1. *Structure of chlorophyll (a) and a chloroplast (b).*
Chlorophyll is found in the membranes of thylakoid sacs.

The name "photosynthesis" actually reflects these two parts: the "photo" (light) part captures energy from sunlight (through the light-dependent reactions), and the "synthesis" part builds sugar (through the Calvin cycle). The light reactions and Calvin cycle can be summed up in one equation of photosynthesis. As you look at the equation below, notice where oxygen, carbon dioxide, sunlight, sugar, and water are placed:

$$6CO_2 \ + \ 6H_2O \ + \ sunlight \ \rightarrow \ C_6H_{12}O_6 \ (sugar) \ + \ 6O_2$$

To make this equation more interesting, think about this: The oxygen in water (H_2O) is actually converted to oxygen gas by photosynthesis. So the oxygen we breathe started off as water in plants! The sugar formed by photosynthesis is later used to build all other carbon-based molecules needed by the plant. So every carbon atom found in a plant—in its sugars, proteins, DNA, and membranes—originally started off as carbon dioxide in the air . . . probably exhaled by an animal!

Today we'll focus on the energy-absorbing chlorophyll molecules that make photosynthesis possible. Chlorophyll collects solar energy, but doesn't actually use every part of sunlight. It only absorbs a few colors or "wavelengths."

Accessory Pigments

Chlorophyll is not the only pigment found in leaves—you'll see today what other pigments are found in spinach (a pretty typical plant). These other **accessory pigments** aid the plant by *absorbing light colors (and energy) that chlorophyll cannot.* Most of the time, these other pigments add up to only a fraction of the amount of chlorophyll, so plants usually just look bright green.

About the Equipment You Will Be Using Today

In today's lab, you will be working with a spectrophotometer.

This experiment uses instructions specific to the ThermoSpectronic Genesys 20 Spectrophotometer in the lab. If you are using a different spectrophotometer, you will need a second set of instructions on how to use your spectrophotometer.

Activity 1: Chromatography of Chlorophyll

Materials

+ Scissors

+ Mortar and pestle

+ 1 chromatography vial (test tube with lid or stopper)

+ 1 strip of chromatography paper

+ 1 ruler

+ 1 fresh spinach leaf

+ Bottle of chromatography solvent (9 petroleum ether : 1 acetone)

+ Capillary tubes

+ Pencil

Caution! Gloves and safety goggles must be worn during this lab. Solvents may produce fumes, and are flammable—keep jars tightly closed.

1. Using a disposable pipette, add 1 mL of chromatography solvent to the chromatography vial, and replace the cap tightly.

2. Set the chromatography vial to the side, and allow it to sit undisturbed until it is needed. (This will allow time for the vial to become saturated with solvent vapors, so that the procedure will work well.)

3. Measure 1 cm from the end of your chromatography strip. (*Be sure to handle the chromatography strip by the edges only. Extra marks or fingerprints will hinder your results!*)

4. At the 1 cm mark, draw a faint pencil line across the width of the strip.

5. Cut two pieces off of the bottom of the chromatography strip to form a pointed end. (See Figure 7-2.)

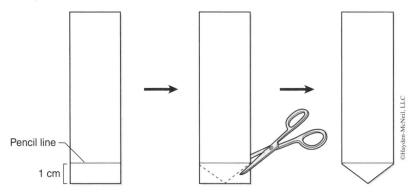

Figure 7-2. *Preparing your chromatography strip.*

6. Grind the spinach leaf (or a few small leaves) using mortar and pestle.

7. Using the capillary tube, transfer some of the slurry over the pencil line of the chromatography strip.

8. Carefully remove the cap from the chromatography vial.

9. Gently place the chromatography strip into the chromatography vial, so that the pointed end is just barely touching the solvent. (*Do not allow the pigment line to come in direct contact with the solvent*—the pigment will dissolve and the procedure will not work!)

10. Immediately cap the chromatography vial and allow it to sit, undisturbed.

11. Observe the solvent moving up the chromatography strip. (The line where the paper is wet with solvent is the "solvent front.") You will be able to see the different plant pigments being separated out along the strip.

12. Watch the chromatography vial until the solvent is approximately 1 cm from the top of the chromatography strip. (*Do not let the solvent migrate off the top of the strip—you will miss some of the results!*) While you wait, start Activity 2 of the lab.

13. Remove the cap of the vial. Use forceps to remove the chromatography strip from the vial. Re-cap the vial immediately. This is your chromatogram.

14. Mark the solvent front with a pencil, immediately after removing the strip. Work quickly; the solvent evaporates fast.

15. Once the strip has dried, use a pencil to mark each pigment band on your chromatography strip, as shown in Figure 7-3.

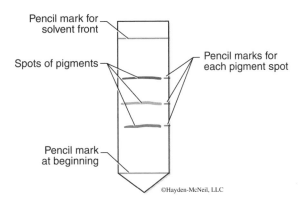

Figure 7-3. *Positions of pigments have been marked on the strip.*

16. List the colors that you observe in Table 7-1.

17. Clean up your work area:

    a. Dispose of the chromatography solvent in a marked waste bottle.

    b. Discard used spinach leaves and chromatography strips in the trash. (If you like, you may keep the chromatography strip!)

PHOTOSYNTHESIS: Activity 1

Name _____

Date _____

Section _____

Table 7-1. *Migration of spinach pigments during chromatography.*

Pigment Color	Pigment Migration (mm)	Solvent Front Migration (mm)	R_f Value

1. Using a ruler, measure the distance from the original pencil line with the spinach extract to the solvent front, and each mark you made for each pigment band. Record these distances in millimeters in Table 7-1.

2. Using the following formula, you can now calculate the R_f value for each pigment on your chromatogram. (No matter how long the paper strip or the position of the solvent front, every pigment will have a standard R_f value. This value can be used to identify the pigment!)

$$R_f = \frac{\text{Distance pigment traveled}}{\text{Distance solvent traveled}}$$

Activity 2: Absorption Spectrum of Chlorophyll

Materials

+ Kimwipes (thin tissue wipes)

+ Fresh spinach

+ Denatured ethanol

+ Mortar and pestle

+ Funnel

+ Glass test tubes

+ Spectrophotometer

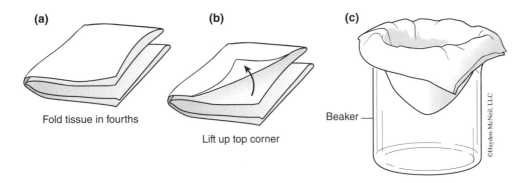

(a) Fold tissue in fourths

(b) Lift up top corner

(c) Beaker

©Hayden-McNeil, LLC

Figure 7-4. *Making a paper funnel.*

Caution! Denatured ethanol is drying to the skin, and contains methanol (a poison). Wear gloves!

PROCEDURE

Before you begin, turn on the spectrophotometer so it can warm up. Your instructor will show you how.

PREPARING THE SAMPLE

1. Fold a Kimwipe in half, and then in half again to form a small square. Pull up one corner of the square to form a simple "funnel," as shown in Figure 7-4. Place this funnel in a small beaker. It's okay if the funnel unfolds, as long as it fits in the beaker and doesn't have holes.

2. Get a tiny piece of spinach no larger than your thumb nail. (If you use too much, you'll probably have to dilute your sample and start over again!)

3. Place the spinach in the bottom of the mortar, and add 10 mL of ethanol. Grind the spinach with the pestle, until no leaf pieces are visible and the liquid is a bright green. Work quickly, before the liquid evaporates!

4. Use a funnel to pour the green liquid through the Kimwipe "funnel" you created earlier (like a coffee filter). You can use a gloved finger to squeeze out the funnel. The goal is to remove any tiny fragments of spinach cells from the liquid, and to get several milliliters of liquid.

5. Pour the liquid into a clean glass test tube, and set it in the test tube rack. The test tube should be at least half full, and the liquid should be visibly green.

6. Use a clean pipette to transfer 5 mL of ethanol into a second clean test tube. This will be your "blank" later on.

USING THE SPECTROPHOTOMETER

1. Use the buttons shown in Figure 7-5 to set the wavelength of your spectrophotometer to 380 nm. (Make sure you use the correct buttons.)

2. Your spectrophotometer should be set up to record *absorbance*. Confirm this by looking at the screen—it should show "0.000 A." (If it shows something else, push the button labeled A/T/C until the correct reading appears.)

3. Press the "0 ABS" ("blank") button. The absorbance reading on the screen should reset itself to zero.

4. Open the lid of the sample chamber. Place a narrow white paper strip into the sample chamber, as your instructor will demonstrate. Look carefully at the card, on the side farthest away from you. You should be able to see a tiny dot of light. Record the color of this light in Table 7-2.

5. With the card still in place, record the absorbance reading here:
What happens to the measured absorbance when something blocks or absorbs the light?

6. Remove the white card from the sample chamber.

7. Insert your plain ethanol "blank" into the sample holder. Set the absorbance to zero as you did before.

NOTE: Setting the blank to zero (or "blanking" the instrument) for a tube of plain ethanol lets us ignore any light absorbed by the solvent or the tube. **IT IS VITAL THAT YOU SET THE "BLANK" TO ZERO EVERY TIME YOU TAKE A MEASUREMENT OR CHANGE THE WAVELENGTH.**

8. Now remove the blank and insert your sample. (Keep the blank, because you'll use it again soon.) Don't push any buttons! Close the lid, and record the "absorbance reading" in Table 7-2.

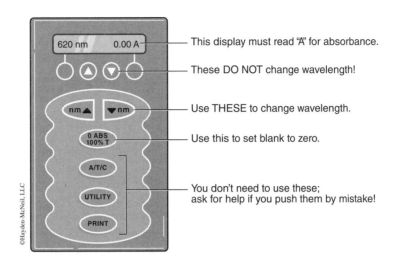

Figure 7-5. *The control panel of your spectrophotometer.*

9. Change the wavelength to the next value in Table 7-2.

   a. Place the "blank" tube in the sample chamber.

   b. Set the blank to zero. (Why do we do this?)

   c. Measure absorbance of your sample, and record it in Table 7-2.

10. For lines in the table that are not shaded, measure the color of light.

    a. Remove any test tubes from the sample chamber.

    b. Insert the white card again, and record the color of light you see in Table 7-2.

    c. Remove the card.

11. Repeat steps 9 and 10 until Table 7-2 is complete.

12. Graph your results on a sheet of graph paper. (Which is the independent variable? Which is the dependent variable?)

13. Clean up your work area:

    a. Dispose of ethanol in the sink or in a waste bottle, as your instructor indicates.

    b. Place all glass test tubes in the broken glass box.

    c. Wash your mortar and pestle, dry them with a paper towel, and return them to your lab table.

PHOTOSYNTHESIS: Activity 2

_____
Name

_____
Date

_____
Section

Table 7-2. _Absorbance spectrum of spinach chlorophyll._

Wavelength (nm)	Color of Light (Skip the Shaded Boxes)	Absorbance Reading (In Absorbence Units, AU)
380		
400		
420		
430		
440		
460		
480		
500		
520		
540		
560		
580		
600		
620		
640		
660		
680		
700		

1. Look at your graph of the absorption spectrum. What colors of light does chorophyll absorb most?

   Which of these colors will provide the most energy to the plant? Explain why.

2. Use the results of your measurements to explain why leaves look green. (Explain in terms of absorbance and wavelength, and whether light is absorbed.)

3. Given the results of your experiments, do you think a plant would grow fastest in red light or green light? Explain.

4. What other pigments are present in the spinach leaf? Give their colors and identify them using Table 7-3. (If you are unsure about some of these, explain why.)

Table 7-3. *R_f values of common plant pigments in PET ether/acetone chromatography.*

Pigment	Color	R_f
Chlorophyll *a*	Blue-green	0.6—0.7
Chlorophyll *b*	Yellow-green	0.4—0.5
β-Carotene	Orange	0.9—1.0
Xanthophylls	Yellow	0.1—0.3

5. Spinach plants have to expend some energy producing these other pigments, so they must be useful to the plant. What purpose do these other pigments serve?

6. In fall, chlorophyll is the first pigment to disappear from dying leaves. Using what you have seen today, and specific vocabulary from the introduction, explain why some leaves turn bright colors in fall.

8
Genetics

---OBJECTIVES---

After completing this lab, you should be able to:

+ Define the laws of segregation and independent assortment.

+ Construct a Punnett square for both a mono- and dihybrid cross.

+ Diagram and evaluate a pedigree.

+ Differentiate between Mendelian and non-Mendelian inheritance.

INTRODUCTION

Before the 1860s people really had no idea what governed the inheritance of traits from parent to offspring. It was then that an Augustinian friar by the name of Gregor Mendel performed a series of now famous experiments on *Pisum sativum* (the garden pea). From these experiments, Mendel laid out the rules for inheritance that formed the foundation of modern genetics, which is why he is credited as being the father of genetics.

In genetics, a character is any factor that can vary between members of a species, and a trait is a specific version of a character. For example, human hairline would be a character and straight hairline would be a trait. One of the reasons Mendel was so successful was that he chose pea plant characters that had exactly two traits. A common example is the character for pea plant flower color and the two traits for it are purple and white.

What would be an example of another human character?

Name at least two traits for the character.

Adapted from *Biology 108 Laboratory Manual*, copyright © 2012 by Dana Kurpius and Fred Vogt, Elgin Community College as modified by the Department of Biology, Northern Virginia Community College, Annandale Campus. Additional duplication is prohibited without written permission of Hayden-McNeil, LLC and Dana Kurpius and Fred Vogt.

A technique that Mendel pioneered was controlled mating through the creation of "female" plants and crossing them with chosen male plants. From these matings, he was able to select specific pea plants that he wanted to cross based on specific traits they had.

> Monsanto is an international company that develops hybrid seed corn for farmers. Can you think of a similar practice (based on Mendel's technique) that they employ in the development of their hybrid seed corns?

An important point to recognize is that Mendel worked with true-breeding strains. To him, this meant that if he allowed a pea plant with a desired trait to self-fertilize it would produce offspring with the same trait as the parent plant 100% of the time. In order to ensure that he had true-breeding strains, he pioneered a genetic technique known as the test cross. He would cross a pea plant displaying the dominant phenotype (but unknown genotype) with a plant displaying the recessive phenotype.

1. For example, when Mendel observed that a pea plant had purple flowers did he automatically know its genotype? Explain.

2. What is the only genotype you will know for certain?

The offspring of this mating would tell him definitively whether or not the dominant pea plant was homozygous recessive or heterozygous for the genotype.

3. Explain why this is true.

With his pea plant experiments, Mendel was trying to elucidate the mechanisms by which offspring inherit their traits from their parents. The specific type of experiment he performed is referred to as a test cross. Specifically, he would mate two plants that differed in either one or two traits and these were called the monohybrid and dihybrid test crosses, respectively. Worth noting is the fact that both plants in the parental generation were true-breeding for the desired trait. From doing these experiments repeatedly, Mendel was able to derive the two fundamental laws of modern genetics.

Mendel's first law is known as the Law of Segregation. In this law, he states that allele pairs separate from one another during the formation of gametes in meiosis. At fertilization, the two alleles are reunited and the zygote is then diploid.

4. Which round of meiosis represents the Law of Segregation?

After performing his dihybrid crosses, he formulated his Law of Independent Assortment, which states that alleles are inherited independently of one another. When Mendel was performing his pea plant experiments in the 1860s, he was not aware of chromosomes and the events of cell division. Today, we know that the behavior of chromosomes during cell division explains Mendel's two laws and is known as the chromosomal basis for the theory of inheritance.

5. What would Mendel have observed if he had inadvertently chosen traits that were controlled by alleles that were found on the same chromosome?

6. What could he have named his law based on this data?

Gregor Mendel's work on the inheritance of traits in pea plants formed the foundation of modern genetics. As such, the phrase "Mendelian genetics" refers to the three main tenets of Mendel's work: a character is controlled by a single gene, there exist only two traits for that character, and one trait exhibits complete dominance over the other. However, there are many different characters in different organisms that do not follow these rules of inheritance. Any character that falls into this category is referred to as non-Mendelian.

Activity 1: Mendelian Genetics

HUMAN GENETICS TASTE KIT

There are many human characters whose inheritance follows Mendelian genetics. In this activity, you will be investigating the presence of three of these genetically controlled traits. Specifically, the ability to taste three different chemicals will be tested among the lab class population. Those chemicals include: thiourea, sodium benzoate, and phenylthiocarbamide (PTC).

Materials

Human Genetics taste Biokit:

+ Sodium benzoate taste papers

+ Thiourea taste papers

+ PTC taste papers

+ Control taste papers

PROCEDURE

1. Obtain a Human Genetics Biokit student guide from your instructor.

2. From the counter, gather the four color coded taste papers: white = control paper, yellow = thiourea, pink = sodium benzoate, blue = phenylthiocarbamide (PTC).

3. First, taste the white control paper.

   What is the point of tasting the control paper first?

4. Take turns within your group to taste the remaining three papers being sure to record your results in the appropriate tables provided.

5. Once all of the lab group members have recorded their individual reaction in the table, be sure to tally the lab group data.

6. Your instructor will collect the individual lab groups' data and tally them on the board. In the space provided in the table, be sure to record those data.

   Based on the data from the class, what is the wild-type trait for each of the three characters tested?

GENETICS

Name

Date

Section

Table 8-1. *PTC.*

	Taster	Nontaster
Individual Reaction		
Group Total		
Class Total		
% Tasters and Nontasters		

Table 8-2. *Thiourea.*

	Taster	Nontaster
Individual Reaction		
Group Total		
Class Total		
% Tasters and Nontasters		

Table 8-3. *Sodium benzoate.*

	T-Bitter	T-Other	T-Salt	T-Sweet	Nontaster
Individual Reaction					
Group Total					
Class Total					
% Tasters and Nontasters					

A male and a female are both heterozygous for the alleles that control PTC tasting. Develop a Punnett square (use the shell below) to help determine the possible genotypes and phenotypes. What is the probability of this couple having a child that can taste PTC? P = the dominant allele and p = the recessive allele. Tasting PTC is dominant to not tasting it.

A female is heterozygous for PTC but cannot taste thiourea. Her husband cannot taste PTC or thiourea. Develop a Punnett square (use the shell below) to help determine what the possible genotypes and phenotypes of the offspring will be.

What is the probability of a child who can taste PTC, but cannot taste thiourea? What is the probability of a child who cannot taste either chemical?

For today's lab, you will be using laptop computers. You may use your own, or one provided by the Biology Department.

OBJECTIVES

After completing this lab, you should be able to:

+ Construct cladograms for a group of species.

+ Use protein databases and phylogenetic tree-drawing software on the Internet.

INTRODUCTION

One of the distinctive aspects of biology is that living organisms change through time. **Phylogenetic systematics** attempts to determine: (1) the evolutionary pathway by which modern species arose; (2) how and to what degree species are related; and (3) what their ancestors may have looked like.

The goal of this lab is to apply phylogenetic systematics to examine the degrees of relatedness among a group of species. In doing so, you will make inferences about the course of evolution. Usually, evolution proceeds far too slowly to be observed directly, but many of the changes that occurred as species diverged are preserved as characteristics in the organisms alive today. First, we'll look at how phylogenetic trees are constructed using the character states of the species under study. Then, we'll look at how bioinformatics databases provide us with data to draw a phylogenetic tree of selected mammals.

Adapted from *BIO 112L Principles of Biology II*, 2007–2009 ed., by Joseph Bundy and The University of North Carolina at Greensboro Biology Department as modified by Ilya Tëmkin. Copyright © 2008 by Hayden-McNeil, LLC. Additional duplication is prohibited without written permission of Hayden-McNeil, LLC.

Activity 1: Drawing Phylogenetic Trees

All animals share a common ancestor in evolutionary history. The evolutionary history of organisms over time is called **phylogeny**. Biologists have used fossilized remains of animals to learn more about the phylogeny of animals, but the fossil record is incomplete for many animal groups. To overcome this obstacle, scientists usually examine shared, homologous features of animals. Animals that have many features in common probably had a fairly recent common ancestor and are considered closely related.

CLADISTIC ANALYSIS

Cladistic analysis is a method of determining evolutionary relatedness based on studying shared characteristics of organisms. In order to reconstruct the phylogeny of a set of organisms we must have an extensive list of **characters** and **character states** for the organisms. Characters are any features or attributes of an organism that form the basis for comparisons. Character states are alternative forms of a character. For instance, in humans "six digits" and "five digits" are character states for the character "number of toes." There are two types of characters that can be used for cladistic analysis: morphological characters (skeletal features, body structures, etc.) and molecular information (DNA sequences, amino acid sequences, etc.). Which type of character to use is up to the researcher.

Scientists use the character states of an organism when making decisions about how closely related organisms are to each other. Phylogenetic systematists recognize two types of character states: **primitive character states** and **derived character states.** Primitive character states are those seen in the earliest ancestors of an organism. For instance, having vertebrae is a primitive character state for mammals, since the earliest mammals had vertebrae. Derived character states are evolutionary innovations that are not seen in the earliest ancestors of an organism. For example, hair is a derived character state in mammals. When a group of organisms share a homologous, derived character state, that character state is called a **synapomorphy**. Feathers are a synapomorphy for birds.

Let's look at a simple cladistic analysis. When we start a cladistic analysis, we begin with a group of organisms called the **ingroup**. In the following example, our ingroup will consist of five vertebrates: lamprey, lion, frog, salmon, and turtle. Next, we pick an **outgroup**, a group of organisms that is thought to be closely related to the ancestor of the ingroup, but is not part of the ingroup itself. It serves as the standard for comparison for the ingroup, showing the systematist what character states are considered to be primitive. For this example, we'll use the lancelet as the outgroup. Lancelets are aquatic chordates that have notochords, as all chordates do, but they lack vertebrae.

Table 9-1. *Character matrix for the ingroup species.*

Species	Hair	Amniotic Eggs	Four Walking Legs	Hinged Jaws	Vertebral Column
Lamprey					X
Lion	X	X	X	X	X
Frog			X	X	X
Salmon				X	X
Turtle		X	X	X	X

Once we've established the ingroup and outgroup, we make a list of characters that we wish to examine. Appropriate characters to use should be homologous and heritable. The characters should show primitive and derived states within the ingroup and they should be stable. A table called a character matrix can help us organize our data concerning character states. If an organism shows a derived character state (that is, the character state is different from the character state of the outgroup), then we will put an "X" in the table. If the character state is primitive, then we will leave that cell empty.

Next, we reorganize this information into a shared character table, where we determine which derived character state is shared by the most members of the ingroup, followed by the second most common shared derived character, then the third most common shared derived character, and so on. The shared character table looks like Table 9-2.

Table 9-2. *Shared character table.*

Shared Character	Lamprey	Lion	Frog	Salmon	Turtle	Branched Off Species
Vertebral Column	X	X	X	X	X	Lancelet
Hinged Jaws		X	X	X	X	Lamprey
Four Walking Legs		X	X		X	Salmon
Amniotic Egg		X			X	Frog
Hair		X				Turtle

Notice how the data have been reorganized for the shared character table. The first row lists "vertebral column" as the most common shared character; all the members of the ingroup have the derived character "vertebral column." The second row lists "hinged jaws" as the second most common shared character (only the lamprey lacks hinged jaws). Three of the animals have four walking legs, two have amniotic eggs, and only one has hair.

The last column, "branched off species" tells us which species from the row above lack the derived character from the current row. So, if you look at the second row—"hinged jaws"—you will notice that lamprey is the "branched off species;" lamprey had an "X" in the row above it (the "vertebral column" row), but that "X" is gone in the "hinged jaw" row. In the "four walking legs" row, salmon is the "branched off species" because there is an "X" in the "hinged jaw" row that is missing in the "four walking legs" row. That pattern continues down the table. The outgroup—in this case, lancelet—is always the "branched off" species for the first row of a shared character table.

The shared character table is used to construct a **cladogram**, a tree-like diagram that illustrates the sequence of evolutionary events that occurred in the lineages making up the ingroup. As you see in Figure 9-1, we start with a simple Y-shaped diagram, illustrating that the outgroup branched off from the organisms in our ingroup and the common ancestor that they all shared at some point in history. Notice that the derived character state "vertebral column" evolved sometime after the lancelet lineage (the outgroup) branched off to evolve independently of the other chordates. That evolutionary change is indicated by a tick mark in the diagram. Every organism "above" that tick mark shares the character state "vertebral column."

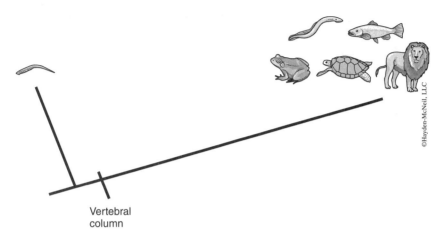

Figure 9-1. *The beginnings of the cladogram.*

The second most common shared character state was "hinged jaws." Notice from the shared character table that lamprey branched off before the hinged jaw condition evolved. So, we can now draw a branch from our main diagonal line for the lamprey and indicate the evolutionary change of "hinged jaws" with a tick mark, as you see in Figure 9-2.

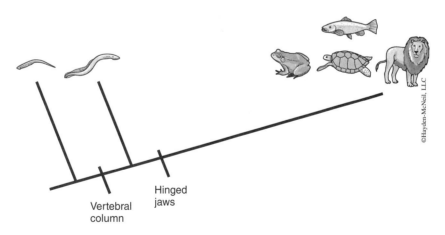

Figure 9-2. *The next step in drawing the cladogram.*

The third most common character state was "four walking legs." The shared character table tells us that salmon branched off before the four walking legs character evolved. So, we can now draw a branch from the main diagonal line for the salmon and indicate the evolutionary change of "four walking legs" with a tick mark (Figure 9-3).

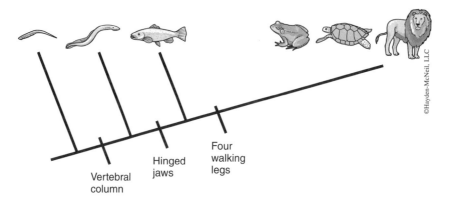

Figure 9-3. *The next step in drawing the cladogram.*

The fourth most common character state was "amniotic eggs." The shared character table tells us that frog branched off before the amniotic egg character evolved. So, we can now draw a branch from the main diagonal line for the frog and indicate the evolutionary change of "amniotic eggs" with a tick mark (Figure 9-4).

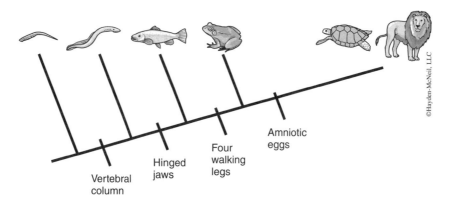

Figure 9-4. *The next step in drawing the cladogram.*

That leaves us with only two animals left in the ingroup to consider: turtle and lion. The shared character table tells us that turtle branched off before the "hair" character evolved. So, we can draw a branch from the main diagonal line for the turtle and indicate the evolutionary change of "hair" with a tick mark (Figure 9-5). The cladogram is now complete for the ingroup.

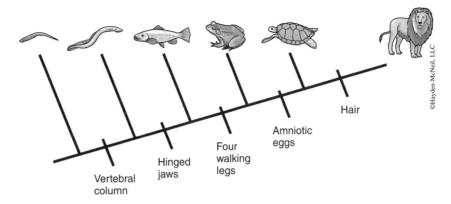

Figure 9-5. *The last step in drawing the cladogram. The cladogram is now complete.*

As we look back at the completed cladogram, we see that all the animals in the ingroup (lamprey, salmon, frog, turtle, and lion) evolved from some common ancestor after that ancestor split from a related group (the outgroup, or lancelet, in our example). The group "lamprey/salmon/frog/turtle/lion" is a **monophyletic group**, meaning that they all descended from a common ancestor. The outgroup split off from the common ancestor of all these animals and *after that*, the common ancestor of the "lamprey/salmon/frog/turtle/lion" group acquired the derived character of vertebral column. How do we know this evolutionary change occurred after the outgroup split off from the ingroup? Because the outgroup still has the primitive state (no vertebral column), while the "lamprey/salmon/frog/turtle/lion" group has the derived state (vertebral column). The ancestor of the lamprey split off, and the common ancestor of the "salmon/frog/turtle/lion" group developed the derived state of hinged jaws. Again, we know that this split occurred before the development of hinged jaws because lampreys don't have hinged jaws, but salmon, frogs, turtles, and lions do. Then, the ancestor of salmon split off, and the derived state "four walking legs" evolved in the "frog/turtle/lion" ancestor. The ancestor of frog branched off, and the derived state "amniotic eggs" evolved in the "turtle/lion" ancestor. The turtle lineage split from the lion lineage before the development of hair in the lion lineage.

The cladogram gives us clues about which species are most closely related. The species with the most recent common ancestor are the ones that share the most derived characters. Turtles and lions are the most related species in our ingroup, since they share four derived characters. Salmon, frogs, turtles, and lions are less related because they share only two derived characters. You would have to go back further in time to find their common ancestor. Lampreys, salmon, frogs, turtles, and lions are only slightly related because they share only one derived character and their common ancestor would have lived long, long ago. Regardless of that, the group "lamprey/salmon/frog/turtle/lion" is monophyletic because they all came from a common ancestor that acquired the derived character "vertebral column" and passed it on to all of them.

Materials

* Cladogram problem handouts

PROCEDURE

You and your lab partner will receive a pair of cladogram problems to solve. Use the information provided as guides to solve the problems. Check with your instructor to see how close you come to the "answers."

PHYLOGENETICS

Name

Date

Section

STUDENT REPORT

Activity 2: Molecular Phylogenies

With advances in technology, it is now possible for biologists to look at changes in biochemistry as measures of evolutionary relatedness. Differences in DNA sequences are good indicators of relatedness. Living things inherit their DNA from their ancestors. Changes in DNA sequences—mutations—change alleles in the gene pool of a population. It is the emergence of new alleles that creates new genotypes. New phenotypes are the result of the expression of new genes. The products of gene expression are proteins. Therefore, changes in DNA sequence ultimately lead to changes in protein construction.

Two species diverge from a common ancestor when mutations occur that result in new phenotypes. The longer that two species diverge from the common ancestor, the more different their DNA sequences (and, consequently, the amino acid sequences of their proteins) will become. Biologists use the similarities between DNA sequences and amino acid sequences in proteins as measures of evolutionary relatedness. For example, molecular biologists have determined that cytochrome *c* is composed of 104 amino acids. When comparing the amino acid sequences of human cytochrome *c* and yeast cytochrome *c*, they find that the sequences differ in 44 amino acids. Human and chimpanzee cytochrome *c* are identical. These data are consolidated with fossil information and morphological comparisons to confirm evolutionary relationships between organisms. Because the amount of data collected from biochemical studies and morphological studies can be enormous, computer programs are now used to generate phylogenetic trees.

We will use a protein database to get information about amino acid sequences for hemoglobin in ungulate mammals. Ungulates are hoofed, herbivorous mammals that can be classified into two major orders: the artiodactyls and the perissodactyls. Artiodactyls have an even number of toes on each foot (either 2 or 4) and include camels, cattle, deer, goats, pigs, and sheep. Perissodactyls have an odd number of toes on each foot and include the modern horses, rhinoceroses, and zebras. After getting the amino acid sequence data, we'll put those data into a computer program that will draw a phylogenetic tree for you.

Materials

+ Computer with Internet access

PROCEDURE

Getting Amino Acid Sequences

"Swiss-Prot" is one of the world's leading protein databases. We will obtain our amino acid sequences from this website.

1. Go to the Swiss-Prot database at http://us.expasy.org/sprot/. The site should look something like Figure 9-6.

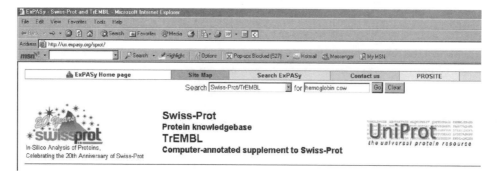

Figure 9-6. *The Swiss-Prot Protein Knowledgebase.*

2. Using the text box near the top of the page, enter the protein you want to find and the organism name. For example, you might enter "hemoglobin bovine" (for hemoglobin from cows). Click the "Go" button. Do not use "and"s or "or"s in Swiss-Prot search boxes.

3. You should get a page that lists several possible proteins, one of which is HBB_BOVIN, the beta chain of cow hemoglobin. Click on that link, and you will be taken to another page that gives you the protein's official name, its synonyms, its gene name, the taxonomy of the animal from which it came, references about how the protein was sequenced, how the protein functions, etc.

Figure 9-7. *Amino acid sequence of the beta chain of bovine hemoglobin, as reported by the Swiss-Prot database.*

4. What you want to know is the amino acid sequence of this protein. Scroll to the very bottom of the page to see that information. Notice that the length of the amino acid sequence is reported, as well as the molecular weight.

5. To the right of the amino acid sequence is a link referring to "FASTA format." FASTA is a common format for presenting DNA or amino acid sequence data to bioinformatics programs. Click on the link to "FASTA format." The format of the data changes to look like Figure 9-8.

```
>sp|P02070|HBB_BOVIN Hemoglobin beta subunit (Hemoglobin beta chain) (Beta-globin) - Bos taurus (Bovine).
MLTAEEKAAVTAFWGKVKVDEVGGEALGRLLVVYPWTQRFFESFGDLSTADAVMNNPKVK
AHGKKVLDSFSNGMKHLDDLKGTFAALSELHCDKLHVDPENFKLLGNVLVVVLARNFGKE
FTPVLQADFQKVVAGVANALAHRYH
```

Figure 9-8. *Amino acid sequence of the beta chain of bovine hemoglobin, shown in FASTA format. (Notice that the amino acid sequence is shown using the International Union of Pure and Applied Chemistry [IUPAC] abbreviations for the amino acid names.)*

We could copy this amino acid sequence, starting at the "MLTA…," onto the Clipboard on the computer and then enter it into bioinformatics programs. Then, we could do another search in Swiss-Prot for another beta chain hemoglobin amino acid sequence for a different organism.

6. Using the "Back" key on your internet browser, go back to the main page for Swiss-Prot and enter "HBB" as your search parameter. Then, click the "Go" button. Notice how many results come back! As you scroll down the page, notice that there are quite a number of hemoglobin beta chains from quite a large number of organisms compiled in the database. You could pull the amino acid sequences for many, many organisms at this point, but we've already done that work for you.

7. Your instructor will provide you with the URL of a website where you can obtain a Word document called "HBB_FASTA_sequences.doc." This file contains the hemoglobin beta chain sequences for cows, horses, sheep, goats, rhinos, camels, pigs, and humans. Open this file, and copy the contents (starting from ">cow" to the end) onto the Clipboard.

Table 9-3. *IUPAC abbreviations for amino acids.*

IUPAC Amino Acid Code	Three-Letter Code	Amino Acid
A	Ala	Alanine
C	Cys	Cysteine
D	Asp	Aspartic Acid
E	Glu	Glutamic Acid
F	Phe	Phenylalanine
G	Gly	Glycine
H	His	Histidine
I	Ile	Isoleucine
K	Lys	Lysine
L	Leu	Leucine
M	Met	Methionine
N	Asn	Asparagine
P	Pro	Proline
Q	Gln	Glutamine
R	Arg	Arginine
S	Ser	Serine
T	Thr	Threonine
V	Val	Valine
W	Trp	Tryptophan
Y	Tyr	Tyrosine

Loading Amino Acid Sequences into a Bioinformatics Program

The next series of steps will take you through entering amino acid sequence data into a popular bioinformatics program called ClustalW. ClustalW is operated by the European Bioinformatics Institute. The program performs alignments of more than two species so that corresponding sections of amino acid chains are compared at the same time. It can determine the relationship between multiple sequences and can cluster them into cladograms or phylograms. That way, biologists can see the degree of relatedness between DNA or protein sequences.

1. Go to the ClustalW website: http://www.ebi.ac.uk/clustalw/index.html. The website should look something like Figure 9-9.

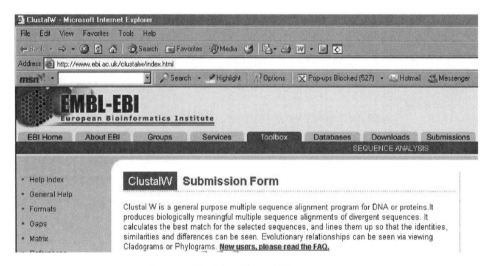

Figure 9-9. *The ClustalW program.*

2. Paste the information you copied from the hemoglobin file into the text box submission form. Change the "Output Order" (just above the text box) from "aligned" to "input." Then click "Run" (located below the text box).

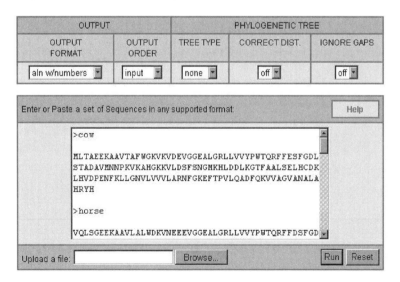

Figure 9-10. *Hemoglobin data is put into the ClustalW program and is ready to run. Notice that the "Output Order" has been changed to "input."*

3. After a short pause, you will get a screen that starts with a table of differences between the different organisms. For the hemoglobin beta chain, the table starts like Figure 9-11.

The results show that the hemoglobin beta chain sequences were 81% identical between cows and horses, and they were 93% identical between cows and sheep.

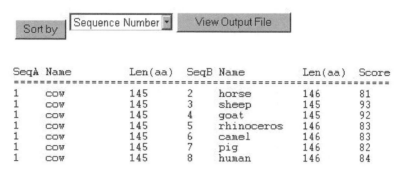

Scores Table

SeqA	Name	Len(aa)	SeqB	Name	Len(aa)	Score
1	cow	145	2	horse	146	81
1	cow	145	3	sheep	145	93
1	cow	145	4	goat	145	92
1	cow	145	5	rhinoceros	146	83
1	cow	145	6	camel	146	83
1	cow	145	7	pig	146	82
1	cow	145	8	human	146	84

Figure 9-11. *Partial output from ClustalW.*

4. Let's look at the Alignment section, where the program attempted to align the hemoglobin beta chain sequences of the animals. We can see how many amino acids have changed from one species to another. We will use the aligned sequences to do the evolutionary comparison.

5. Highlight all the text starting with "Clustal W (1.82) multiple sequence alignment" and ending with the last line of the alignment. Copy all this text into your Clipboard.

Alignment

```
CLUSTAL W (1.82) multiple sequence alignment

cow         -MLTAEEKAAVTAFWGKVKVDEVGGEALGRLLVVYPWTQRFFESFGDLSTADAVMNNPKV 59
horse       VQLSGEEKAAVLALWDKVNEEEVGGEALGRLLVVYPWTQRFFDSFGDLSNPGAVMGNPKV 60
sheep       -MLTAEEKAAVTGFWGKVKVDEVGGEALGRLLVVYPWTQRFFEHFGDLSNADAVMNNPKV 59
goat        -MLTAEEKAAVTGFWGKVKVDEVGAEALGRLLVVYPWTQRFFEHFGDLSSADAVMNNAKV 59
rhinoceros  VELTAEEKAAVLALWDKVKEDEVGGEALGRLLVVYPWTQRFFDSFGDLSTPAAVMGNAKV 60
camel       VHLSGDEKNAVHGLWSKVKVDEVGGEALGRLLVVYPWTRRFFESFGDLSTADAVMGNPKV 60
pig         VHLSAEEKEAVLGLWGKVNVDEVGGEALGRLLVVYPWTQRFFESFGDLSNADAVMGNPKV 60
human       VHLTPEEKSAVTALWGKVNVDEVGGEALGRLLVVYPWTQRFFESFGDLSTPDAVMGNPKV 60
            *:  :** **  :*.**:  :*** .************:***  *****.. ***.*.**
```

Figure 9-12. *Partial sequence alignment output from ClustalW. Key to symbols in the alignment data:* = all the species had an identical amino acid in that spot: = all the amino acids in that spot were similar. = the amino acids in that spot were less similar space = one or more amino acids in that spot wre markedly different.*

6. Use the "Back" button on your internet browser to return to the ClustalW page where you entered your protein sequences. Clear all that text and paste in the contents of your Clipboard. Then change the ClustalW parameters (last line above the text box) like Figure 9-13.

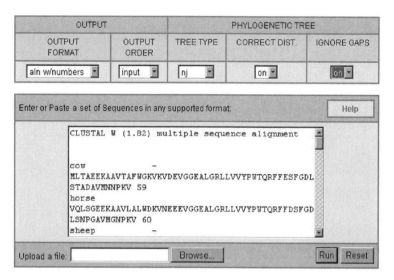

Figure 9-13. *Alignment data entered into ClustalW input text box, with changes made to paramters. Change "Tree Type" to "nj" (= "neighbor-joining," a technique for drawing phylogenetic trees). Change "Correct Distance" and "Ignor Gaps" to "on" (this will help elimate some inaccuracies in the input data).*

7. Click "Run." When the output is delivered, scroll down to the bottom of the page and find the tree-like cladogram. Click the button "Show as a Phylogram Tree." The branches of the tree group related sequences, and the lengths of the branches indicate degree of difference between the sequences. To help you understand how the phylogram is structured, Figure 9-14 shows a phylogram using triosephosphate isomerase, an enzyme used in glycolysis.

Phylogram

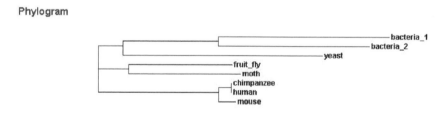

Figure 9-14. *Phylogram output, drawn by ClustalW using a non-hemoglobin example and several different species.*

Notice that the triosephosphate isomerase of humans and chimpanzees are extremely similar, and that these enzymes are rather similar to the one found in mice. The mammalian version of this enzyme is very different from bacterial triosephosphate isomerase. Notice the long branches of the bacterial enzymes; this indicates that the bacterial enzymes differ from each other more than the insect (fruit fly and moth) versions of the enzyme differ from each other.

■ OBSERVATIONS

In the space below, sketch the phylogram that ClustalW created using the hemoglobin beta chain data that you entered.

PHYLOGENETICS

Name _____

Date _____

Section _____

1. Looking back at the hemoglobin output, which two ungulate species are most closely related?

2. Which species is most closely related to humans?

3. If a phylogenetic tree is meant to be a reconstruction of an evolutionary sequence, can there be more than one correct set of relationships among a group of species? Why or why not?

10
Population Genetics

OBJECTIVES

After completing this lab, you should be able to:

+ Describe the conditions for a population to be in Hardy-Weinberg equilibrium.

+ Describe the importance of genetic variation to evolution and explain how changes in gene frequency can be used to study evolution.

+ Conduct electrophoresis to examine human hemoglobin genotypes.

+ Conduct a simulation to investigate the effects of selection on allelic frequencies of a population.

+ Conduct a simulation to investigate the effects of genetic drift on allelic frequencies of a population.

+ Explain heterozygote advantage and how it may maintain alleles in a population.

INTRODUCTION

Charles Darwin (1859) theorized descent with modification by means of **natural selection** to explain the diversity of life observed in modern and geologic eras. Darwin was not initially familiar with the laws of genetic inheritance since Gregor Mendel's *Experiments in Plant Hybridization*, which identified the two basic laws of inheritance, was not published until 1865. Darwin observed that environmental factors affected individual survival. He proposed that individuals with traits that aided survival were more likely to survive to pass the favored traits to the next generation. We call these traits genes and know genetic variation to be a key factor in evolution. The basis of Darwin's theory of evolution by natural selection is heritable, or genetic, variation. All organisms exhibit genetic variation. Recall from your study of Mendelian genetics that the expression of an individual's genotype is its phenotype.

Adapted from *Laboratory Manual for Biology 112*, 7th ed., copyright © 2012 by Tonna Harris-Haller, and for Sickle-Cell Alleles copyright © 2011 by SimBiotic Software for Teaching and Research, Inc., as modified by the Department of Biology, Northern Virginia Community College, Annandale Campus. Additional duplication is prohibited without written permission of Hayden-McNeil, LLC, Tonna Harris-Haller and SimBiotic Software for Teaching and Research, Inc.

Although individuals show genotypic variation, the individual does NOT evolve. Evolution results from changes in allele or gene frequencies in **populations**. A population is a group of interbreeding individuals of the same species that produce fertile offspring. For example, the elk herd living in Rocky Mountain National Park, Colorado, is descended from individuals that were transplanted from the Yellowstone, Wyoming, elk herd approximately 75 years ago (Figure 10-1). Although they share a common origin, these herds are geographically isolated so they no longer interbreed. In time, the two populations may diverge genetically. Scientists that study evolution in living populations look at the genetic variation of the individuals that constitute that population. This study is called **population genetics**.

Figure 10-1. *Rocky Mountain Elk herd.*

The sum of all the alleles in a population and their relative proportions is a population's **gene pool**. A gene pool is studied by following the **frequency** of an allele through multiple generations. It is possible to use the laws of probability to model **evolution** as the change in allele frequency between generations.

THE HARDY-WEINBERG EQUILIBRIUM

Although individual genetic variability provides the basis for evolution, variability alone does not guarantee a population will evolve. The Hardy-Weinberg equilibrium models a sexually reproducing population with stable allele frequencies. A theoretical population in Hardy-Weinberg equilibrium is **not** evolving because its allele frequencies do not change between generations. There are five assumptions for a population to be in Hardy-Weinberg equilibrium:

1. **Large population size.** Populations must be large enough so random events do not change allele frequency.

2. **No immigration or emigration.** There must be no transport of alleles into or out of the population through movement of individuals.

3. **No genetic mutations.** Mutation could add new alleles and disrupt or prevent genetic equilibrium.

4. **Random mating.** All individuals within a population must have an equal probability of mating.

5. **No natural selection.** All phenotypes must have equal reproductive success.

Populations that meet these assumptions are in Hardy-Weinberg equilibrium and are not evolving. However, few, if any, natural populations meet these conditions. The value of the Hardy-Weinberg formula is not that it can be used to describe natural populations, but that it can be used as a null hypothesis (i.e., evolution is NOT occurring). This makes it possible to test whether evolution is occurring by calculating changes in allele frequencies in a population and comparing those values to the predicted frequencies for a population in Hardy-Weinberg equilibrium.

The Hardy-Weinberg model is a simple equation with some specific terminology. Consider the simplest case, where a chromosome locus has two alleles—one allele is dominant and the other is recessive. The frequency of the **dominant allele** (A) in the population is represented by "p" and the frequency of the **recessive allele** (a) is represented by "q". The sum of the frequencies for any pair of alleles always equals one:

$$\text{Allele frequencies: } p + q = 1$$

The frequency of (A) equals the fraction of all alleles in the population's gene pool that are (A). For example, if all individuals in a population are heterozygous (Aa), then p [A] is 0.5 because *half the alleles* are (A).

A **genotypic frequency** is the percentage of the population with a specific genotype. If a population is in Hardy-Weinberg equilibrium, the genotypic frequencies can be calculated by using the expansion of the Hardy-Weinberg binomial where the frequency of the AA genotype is p^2; the frequency of the heterozygous genotype Aa is 2pq; and the frequency of aa is q^2:

$$\text{Hardy-Weinberg equation: } p^2 + 2pq + q^2 = 1$$

You can use the Hardy-Weinberg equation to estimate allelic frequencies where the genotypic frequencies are partially unknown and **Hardy-Weinberg equilibrium is assumed.** For example: Suppose AA and Aa hamsters are brown while aa hamsters are cream colored. We know that 20% of Texas-bred hamsters are cream colored. Assuming the population is in Hardy-Weinberg equilibrium for coat color, you can estimate the allelic and genotypic frequencies for the population as follows:

+ Determine allelic frequencies for the Texas hamster population in Hardy-Weinberg equilibrium.

   q^2 (frequency of aa) = 0.20

   q = square root of .20 = 0.45

   p = 1 − q = 0.55

If we know the genotypic frequencies in a population, then we can determine if the *observed* frequencies agree with the *expected* frequencies for a population in Hardy-Weinberg equilibrium.

- Determine the expected genotypic frequencies if the hamster population is at Hardy-Weinberg equilibrium.

  Expected frequency of AA = $p^2 = 0.55^2 = 0.30$

  Expected frequency of Aa = $2pq = 2(.55 \times .45) = 0.50$

  Expected frequency of aa = $q^2 = 0.20$

- Your study of the natural hamster population yields observed genotypic frequencies of 60% AA, 20% Aa, and 20% aa. Compare the observed genotypic frequencies with the expected frequencies for a population in Hardy-Weinberg equilibrium.

Table 10-1.

Genotype	Observed	Expected
AA	0.60	0.30
Aa	0.20	0.50
aa	0.20	0.20

Is this population in Hardy-Weinberg equilibrium?

Is it likely this population is experiencing evolution as defined by changes in allele frequencies between generations?

Activity 1: Examining Variability in a Sample Population

The ability to taste common preservatives in foods varies among humans. The chemicals we will study are sodium benzoate, thiourea, and phenylthiocarbamide (PTC). The ability to taste these chemicals may have once helped hunter/gatherer humans avoid toxic foods. In modern diets, the ability to taste these chemicals may result in avoidance of some fruits and vegetables that can result in diet-related diseases.

- **Hint:** You may calculate **allelic** frequencies whenever genotypic frequencies are known regardless of whether a population is in Hardy-Weinberg equilibrium.

- You may calculate **genotypic** frequencies from allelic frequencies *only* if a population is assumed to be in Hardy-Weinberg equilibrium.

- You may estimate both **allelic and genotypic** frequencies from the percentage of homozygous recessive individuals *only* if the population is assumed to be in Hardy-Weinberg equilibrium.

Taste detection in these cases follows Mendelian inheritance rules for dominant/recessive alleles. Individuals who taste these chemicals are homozygous dominant, or heterozygous for the taste allele for that chemical. Homozygous recessive individuals will not taste the chemical.

The class will serve as a sample population. You will estimate the allelic frequencies for the genes that control the ability to taste PTC, thiourea, and sodium benzoate for this population. A taste reaction indicates either a homozygous dominant (frequency = p^2) or heterozygous genotype (frequency = $2pq$). The inability to taste a chemical indicates the presence of a homozygous recessive genotype (frequency = q^2).

PROCEDURE

1. Sample a taste paper for each substance and record the results in Table 10-2. Rinse with water between tests. If you have ANY doubt as to whether you taste something, then you are a nontaster.

How did the PTC taste?

What is your possible genotype?

How did the thiourea taste?

What is your possible genotype?

How did the sodium benzoate taste?

What is your possible genotype?

Sodium benzoate may taste salty, sweet, sour, or bitter. If your dietary preferences differ from other family members, it may be because of genetic differences in the way sodium benzoate is detected.

POPULATION GENETICS

Name

Date

Section

1. Enter your data in the data table and transfer the class data to Table 10-2. Record the phenotype data for your classmates.

Table 10-2. *Class taste data.*

	You	Number of Tasters	Number of Nontasters	Number of Students
Thiourea				
Sodium Benzoate				
PTC				
Total				

2. Record the class data in Table 10-3. Calculate the phenotypic frequency of tasters ($p^2 + 2pq$) by dividing the number of tasters in the class by the total number of students in the class.

   Why are both p^2 and $2pq$ included in the taster phenotype?

3. Calculate the phenotypic frequency of nontasters (q^2) by dividing the number of nontasters by the total number of students in the class. Enter the data in Table 10-3.

4. Calculate the frequencies (p and q) of the alleles for each chemical and record the calculations in Table 10-3 (see example on the next page).

5. Use the data on the North American population to calculate the expected frequencies (p and q) of the PTC alleles and record the values in Table 10-3.

    a. How do the frequencies for the class compare with the frequencies for the North American population?

    b. Is the class in Hardy-Weinberg equilibrium?

Table 10-3. *Phenotypic and allelic frequencies of tasters and nontasters for PTC.*

		Phenotype		Allelic Frequency	
		Tasters ($p^2 + 2pq$)	Nontasters (q^2)	p	q
Thiourea	Class				
Sodium Benzoate	Class				
PTC	Class				
	North American Population	0.55			

6. Although about 55% of the overall North American population are PTC tasters, approximately 70% of the North American caucasian population are tasters.

    a. If the class frequencies do not match the expected values for the overall population, what other factor(s) might contribute to the discrepancy?

    b. How might these data be used to plan a marketing campaign for a new diet soft drink that uses sodium benzoate as a preservative?

Example

The ability to taste PTC is due to a dominant allele T. Suppose 120 students conducted the taste test. Eighty-four students were able to taste PTC and thirty-six could not. Calculate the frequencies of T and t as follows:

Because we do not know the genotypic frequencies of the population, we *must assume* the population is in Hardy-Weinberg equilibrium in order to calculate allelic frequencies.

Since the frequency of (tt) = q^2 = 36/120 = 0.30, then the square root of q^2 = q = 0.547.

Since q = 0.547, then p = 1 – q = 1 – 0.547 = 0.453. Therefore the frequency of (T) = p = 0.453.

Given that p = 0.453 and q = 0.547...

...the frequency of (TT) = p^2 = 0.453^2 = 0.205

...the frequency of (Tt) = 2pq = 2 × 0.453 × 0.547 = 0.496

...the frequency of (tt) = q^2 = 0.30

Given these frequencies, and assuming the population is in Hardy-Weinberg equilibrium, we expect the following genotypes in the population of 120 students.

TT = 0.205(120) = 25 students

Tt = 0.496(120) = 59 students

tt = 0.30(120) = 36 students

7. Given a population of 100 individuals where 15 are AA, 25 are Aa, and 60 are aa, what is the frequency of allele "A" and the frequency of allele "a"?

8. Does this population appear to be at Hardy-Weinberg equilibrium?

9. Why is genetic drift more pronounced in small populations?

10. Explain how the heterozygote advantage can maintain a deleterious allele in a population.

11. What is the role of heritable variation in natural selection?

12. What is meant by reproductive "fitness"?